THE FINAL EXAM

General Class Test Guide

by
Dick Bash - KL7IHP

Bash Educational Services

P.O. Box 2115 • San Leandro, California 94577 • USA

ABOUT THE AUTHOR

Dick was born and raised in the Indianapolis, Indiana area and attended college at Indiana University and Purdue University and did his graduate work at the University of Southern California. Graduating from Purdue in January, 1972, he combined his interest in teaching and aviation by specializing in classroom instruction on jet aircraft, such as the Learjet and the Boeing 727. It was while attending Purdue that Dick obtained his Technician Class License.

After moving to Alaska in 1974, he worked as a flight engineer and also acquired his KL7IHP call sign. Still a Technician, he let his interest in Amateur Radio lapse but kept his license current in hopes he would get back on the air. After living overseas, where he flew for various airlines as a Boeing 707 and 727 flight engineer, he returned to the U.S. and renewed his interest in ham radio, determined to get his code speed up and obtain the General Class License.

After struggling with the code he received his General Class license and went on to pursue the Advanced. Suffering the same fate as 69% of the other applicants, he promptly failed the written exam. Getting together with several other hams in the San Francisco area, he studied and researched the material on the exam and finally passed it. Feeling that it was unfair to have 7 out of 10 hams fail the test, he wrote the series **THE FINAL EXAM** in hopes that other hams would have an easier time preparing for the exam. Your comments on how to help Dick make this the best manual in the country are always welcome. Send your comments to the address on the form in the back of the manual.

Dick's station consists of a Kenwood TS-180S and a Hy-Gain TH3MK3 up 32 feet. His 2 meter radio is a Kenwood TR-2400. Feeling that we have to support 10 meters or lose it, he is around 28.600 mHz when he has some free time or on 14.280 or 14.240 mHz. Between the fun of running his company and playing with his Apple II Plus computer, he stays busy. Also he still enjoys flying and teaching aviation related subjects at Sierra Academy of Aeronautics at Oakland Airport. He worked 1,128 contacts while at Kwajalein Island and his Marshall Island callsign is KX6QK.

PREFACE

In August, 1979 a revolution slowly began as a group of hams in the San Francisco Bay area decided that the failure rate on the F.C.C. amateur radio exams was extraordinarily high (69%). In order to combat this failure rate and break the grip it was holding on the growth of ham radio, we began publishing **THE FINAL EXAM.** The material for the book was obtained by interviewing applicants for the exams and collecting the questions they had on their exams. These applicants remembered the questions and answers and we researched the material and printed the manuals. People began passing the Advanced Class written exam who had failed it four or more times in the past.

The principle reason for their failure was not that they didn't study. It was because the material they studied was not on the exams and there was no single text that contained all (or even most) of the material the F.C.C. was asking questions about. By late May, 1980 the passing rate nationwide was 55% instead of 31%. The effect of our manuals was being felt by the government, clubs, other publishers, the ham population in general, amateur radio instructors, and dealers across the country. The "established" publishers were (and still are) against our method. Only two publishers (CQ Magazine and Worldradio) would/will carry our advertisements. We have seen deceit, lies, slander, and confusion hurled at us and we were tempted to give up a multitude of times.

But daily we received the thanks of hams whose backgrounds ranged from an astronaut to bus driver to nuclear scientist to high school janitor. Our phone was busy constantly answering the many questions that came from these supporters. But for their unfailing support, we would have quit and resigned ourselves to the fact that "tradition" was king. Our budget and income were stretched to ridiculous limits. Our staff consisted of volunteers (and still does for the most part) who wanted to make some contribution for the greater good of ham radio.

That brings us to this printing and you. Behind this preface you will find the most accurate test guide in the United States. It is by hams and for hams. We're still a tiny operation and it's the little guy's way of entering the world of hams and the friendships that spring from that. We give you a personal touch that the major publishers can't give. Your predecessors have made this manual possible, as will you make the next version possible. We beg you not to copy the manual because it is the only income we have. We don't publish a magazine or manufacture things on the side. We just do one thing and we do that well: use standard military intelligence procedures to collect and disseminate the data. Our research staff is getting bigger and we're going to do some exciting things soon.

If we are ever successful, it will be because of you, the individual ham. We have vowed not to abuse the trust and friendship you have extended us and welcome any comments you might have on how we can better serve you. Beginning soon we will monitor various 2 meter and h.f. frequencies so you can call in and chat (no business, please). Thanks a million for your support and rest assured that we are working literally day and night to produce the finest (if not necessarily the prettiest) manuals around.

Turn the pages now and embark upon the study that will get you upgraded. Remember: **Upgrading shouldn't be degrading.** From now on it won't be!

Dick

Richard M. Bash - KL7IHP
San Leandro, California

HOW TO TAKE THE $%#&! MORSE CODE TEST

Here's a recipe for successfully passing the F.C.C.'s 13 word per minute code test that you'll be taking. We wrote this because there have been so many folks contacting us who we know can copy code well but seem to have no small amount of trouble doing so under the rigors of being inside the F.C.C.'s fun and games room! So, I ask some of the geniuses at the University of California (Berkeley) Psychology Department to come up with something to help the folks who suffer from this fatal illness. Here's their solution. We've tried it with many other aspiring General Class licensees and it works. It'll work for you, too (if you will let it)! Nuff said!

=.=

1. First, make sure you can copy the code at the prescribed speed. We find that if you can copy 10 words per minute at 100% copy then you'll pass the exam if you will follow these guidelines. Build your speed up to this level before you even **think** about going to visit the guardians of our airwaves.

2. You will be listening to a cassette recorder sitting on a nearby desk **or** you'll be wearing a lovely pair of antiquated earphones (that were old during the 2nd World War!). If you will be listening to code from a recorder without having to wear the headset, then make sure that you get a seat **near** the recorder itself. You'll get your choice of seats if you are early enough arriving to get at the head of the line. If you get a seat near the recorder, avoid having other folks sit in your lap!

3. For the first minute of the recording you will hear a practice message; we encourage you to copy this message even though it doesn't count for anything (except more practice!). After the one minute of practice you will be given the group of 6 letters (all V's) to indicate the start of the "for real" test. The message is nothing more than a regular QSO (one sided) that lasts approximately 5 minutes. If you followed Dick's

suggestions on how to prepare for the code requirement then you'll find that this is just another QSO. This is where all those "on-the-air" QSO's you did will pay off. After the tape containing the message is finished, you will be given a sheet of paper with 10 questions on it.

4. You will be asked questions about the QSO and that'll be such things as the callsigns of the two stations, the QTH, the names of the two hams, the weather, the type of radio in use, the type of antenna and antenna height, the job of the guy sending the code, his type of license and how long he's had it, the power of the station in watts, the age of the sender, the temperature, the RST report, and the reason for terminating the QSO. You'll get 10 questions out of this. As you can see, you'd **better** be able to copy numbers. So, learn the numbers, **learn the numbers, LEARN THE NUMBERS!!!!!** You must get 7 of the 10 questions correct to pass this exam.

5. A major secret in taking these type of exams is having the ability to relax. That only comes from being properly prepared. You've copied dozens of messages **like this one**, so why get all tensed up over it? If you hear a letter you don't recall, then skip it and continue copying. If you miss the next letter, no sweat - keep copying and writing. Get the third letter, though! When I was taking the Extra Class code test I **froze**; the only letter I got in a string of letters was an "e". On the 10 question test they asked me for the sender's name and only one name had an "e" in it: Fred. I guess I got the answer right for all of the wrong reasons, but I got it right nonetheless and my license says nothing about how slick I am with Morse code! So, just sit there and write, write, and write some more (until the tape stops). If you miss something, then press on. If you got F--d for the name you would know it wasn't Bill, John, or Frank, wouldn't you? Don't give in to that feeling that all is lost just because you miss a letter or two (but **not** three).

6. Do **NOT** try to read the material, just write down what you hear. You probably do not have the ability yet to do that, so quit trying, for pity's sake! You will miss letters if you try to make sense of what you're writing. There will be plenty of time for the study of your writing later. There is **no** time for it during the time that the tape is playing. Also be aware that you are not being graded on how neat and tidy your notes are, just on whether you marked the right letter down for a choice.

7. The girl only reads what is on your answer sheet, not what's in your head. Your chances of making another failure in the F.C.C. office improves quite a bit if she cannot read your writing. Be neat with your lettering of the answers.

8. The questions being asked will be given in the same order as the information appeared in the message. This means that the questions about the callsigns and the names involved will be at the front of the test and not half way through the exam. This information can be used to your advantage. If your question is asking for the class of license and you missed a bunch of letters, then do not look in the beginning of the QSO for clues. This information is probably at least half way through the QSO (or even, perhaps, closer to the end of the QSO).

So, girls and boys, that is what the folks who know recommend and their pearls of wisdom are worth paying attention to. Try our system if you're having trouble. For those of you geniuses who copy effortlessly (attention male chauvanist pigs: most of them are YL's/XYL's), just sit down and start writing. The rest of you, plug away and pound that brass!

HOW TO TAKE THE F.C.C. TEST

This examination can be very rough for someone who's not "test savvy". You may have heard that there is a trick to passing a multiple choice type examination and I agree.

Firstly, the night before the exam, get at least 7 hours of sleep and get up about 6 A.M. (that's the price of success, friend). Secondly, I want you to get a **decent** breakfast so that your blood sugar level isn't too low. Thirdly, re-read this **entire** examination guide. Finally, **write** out each of the formulas that you need to memorize about 6 times each. It'll help you remember them.

When you arrive at the testing facility, you might as well relax because you are going to pass and being relaxed about the inevitable makes good sense. You came to take a test, so let's get it over with. Look at all the DX just waiting for you!

When you are given your exam, sit down and, on the scratch paper, write out (from memory) all of the formulas IMMEDIATELY! Next, start with the first question. Read it. Attention speed readers: slow down to about 250 w.p.m. If you cannot answer the question in the same amount of time that it took you to read the question, then SKIP IT and just go on to the next question. Skip all of the questions involving calculations and or schematics, no matter how easy they might be. When you get to the last question you have probably used up about 20 minutes or so and answered around half of the questions. Now go back to the first question you skipped and go over it again. If it's a calculation or a schematic — SKIP IT! Then go on to the next question that you skipped on your first pass through the exam. When you've made two passes through the exam, start at the front of the exam again and include all of the calculations. If you have trouble with one SKIP IT and press on! The fourth pass will take in the schematics. By the time you've finished this pass, you probably have 25-35 questions finished. STOP!! **Stand up and stretch** and then sit back down and finish up the exam.

I like to take hard candy with me to the exam to keep my mouth wet. Seems to help a bit. Smokers, take some gum or Life-Savers. Also remember that the guy who wrote the test probably knows less about radio then you do, so **relax**.

If you've read this exam guide about **10 times** or so, the answers to the questions will tend to jump at you. **NEVER** change an answer. Invariably, you'll change it from a right answer to a wrong one.

On those new questions or ones you can't remember the answer to (probably because you didn't read through this manual **enough** times), first eliminate all of the obviously wrong answers. That'll generally leave two to choose from. One of the two choices may be a general misconception. Read carefully. Answers hat contain the words "always", "must", "only", or "never" are incorrect about 75% of the time, so keep your guard up on those. Look for key words in the answer. On calculations, have a ballpark idea of what the answer **should** be. Always use a calculator and be comfortable using it too. When in doubt, after you've done all of this and still can't figure it out — GUESS! An **intelligent** guess involves all of the above. If you have a so-called "hunch", play it as a last resort. But be sure to *put some kind of answer down*!

After turning in the exam and getting your score, leave the room and write down all you can remember, for your sake, mine, and the other hams. Be sure to write down the easy questions and *also* ones that appear in this manual. That'll serve as a confidence builder for you. If you want to participate in keeping this manual up to date (and I sure hope you will!), then complete the form in the back of this manual and return it to me. If you take the guide to the exam with you, carry it in a paper sack and leave it with the person giving the exams when you take the test. Don't worry about the F.C.C. seeing your manual. I can assure you that they are only too aware of its existence.

Some of the things I've mentioned here are obvious and others corny. TRUST ME! This system was developed for foreign students whose English was "none too good" and it works for them. It'll work for you too. Once again, **spend the time studying** the manual and believe you're going to pass, because YOU ARE! Good luck.

1. Which of the following is correct regarding radiotele-printing?

   Special tones may be used to activate or turn on a remotely controlled printer.

2. What is the correct definition of "power factor"?

   There are three (3) correct definitions. Know them all! First of all, it's the cosine of the phase angle between the voltage and the current (thought you'd like that). Secondly, it can be termed the ratio between the resistance and reactance. Lastly, we can call it the ratio of true power to apparent power. Please advise which defintion appears on your test. In the past, the Commission has used the "cosine of the phase angle between the voltage and the current" definition.

3. How much power input to the finals may a General use on 7.125 MHz?

   Sucker question!!! This is a Novice frequency so you can't exceed 250 watts. Look out!

4. Refer to the following schematic. What is the purpose of the zener diode in this schematic?

   It provides a "reference voltage" to the transistor.

5. What type of antenna would you use to minimize man - made noise?

   A horizontally polarized antenna. This is because man - made noise tends to be vertically polarized and the use of a horizontal antenna minimizes it.

6. What is the definition of "maximum useable frequency" (MUF)?

   It is the highest frequency that you can operate at which permits radio signals to be transmitted at one position and received at a second, more distant point (beyond the ground wave range), by refracting off the ionosphere. It is possible that the test could say "reflecting" instead of "refracting". It used to be that way on the previous exams for the Advanced Class.

7. What is the length, in meters, of a quarter wavelength piece of transmission line that has a velocity factor of 0.66 at a frequency of 14.10 MHz?

   This looks a lot more complicated than what it is, so relax. If you will closely follow the necessary steps, we'll quickly get a solution. First of all, I should explain what is meant by "velocity factor". Out in space, radio waves go zipping along at the speed of light (about 186,000 miles per second or 300,000 kilometers per second). However, when a radio wave travels in something other than a vacuum it goes slower than the speed of light. We express the velocity of a radio wave as a fraction of the speed of light, where 1.0 is equal to the speed of light in a vacuum. In a piece of coax like RG-58, the velocity factor is 0.66 and that means the radio waves move through it at 2/3 of the speed of light. So much for velocity factor. Every substance has one!

Now, for the math:

$$\text{Quarter wavelength in feet} = \frac{\dfrac{984 \times \text{velocity factor}}{\text{frequency in MHz}}}{4}$$

$$\text{Quarter wavelength in feet} = \frac{\dfrac{984 \times .66}{14.10}}{4}$$

$$\text{Quarter wavelength in feet} = \frac{\dfrac{649.44}{14.10}}{4}$$

$$\text{Quarter wavelength in feet} = \frac{46.059574}{4}$$

Quarter wavelength in feet   =   11.514893

The question requires the answer in *meters*, not feet. To get *meters* out of this mess, *divide* the number of feet by 3.2808 (because there are 3.2808 feet in one meter). The answer is 3.509782 meters! (3.51 for our friends in Washington).

8. When do you *NOT* need to give your callsign?

When you are transmitting with an average (mean) output power of one (1) watt or less and the transmissions are directed only to a remote model craft or vehicle, *provided* a transmitter identification card or a plate made of a *durable* substance, indicating the station callsign and the licensee's name and address, is affixed to the transmitter.

9. What is splatter and how can it be prevented?

"Splatter" is a term used to describe the spurious emissions that result when you overmodulate. To prevent splatter, all we have to do is prevent overmodulation. Commonly this is done by installing an RF clipper in the transmitter to clip the waveform and prevent any modulation from exceeding 100%. The clipped signal is then run through a filter. The clipper is installed by the manufacturer and is standard equipment in a lot of radios. The problem with clipping is that excessive clipping can cause a distorted signal.

10. What is the length of one side of a quad antenna?

It is one quarter (1/4) wavelength long.

11. Which of the following figures is correctly portraying a full wave bridge rectifier?

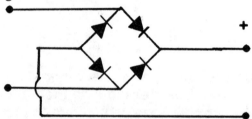

This is the correct illustration for a full wave bridge rectifier. The easy way to identify it is to note that *all* of the diodes (represented by the triangular symbols) must be pointing in the same direction *and* that they must all be pointing towards the plus sign. On the exam, be alert for them to have the diodes pointing 4 different ways.

A full wave bridge rectifier is a device that is used to change alternating current (AC) into direct current (DC). The advantage of this circuit is that it is a bit easier to filter this DC current than it is with other rectifiers that are of a half wave variety (discussion of a half wave rectifier will follow shortly).It is a part of the system that makes up a power supply that will produce very smooth (called "ripple free") DC.

12. Refer to the following schematic. What is being shown here?

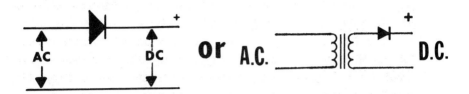

This is a half wave rectifier. Like the full wave bridge rectifier, it will produce DC from AC but it does not produce as smooth a DC as the full wave produces. Also, the average value of the current pulses, as pointed out on page 195 of Shrader's, will be half that of the full wave bridge rectifier. The half wave rectifier is, naturally, less complicated than the full wave bridge rectifier.

13. What are two ratings on a diode that must be observed?

The peak inverse voltage (PIV) and the maximum current. Exceeding the PIV rating can result in a spark (in a tube) going from the plate toward the cathode and damaging the cathode. PIV is the voltage that exists when the plate is negative and that in turn happens during the negative half of the AC cycle. You can also damage a diode if you try to run too much current through it, so the manufacturer puts a limit on the amount of the current. Let me know if they say "peak reverse voltage".

14. When do the F₁ and F₂ layers in the ionosphere exist?

The F layer of the ionosphere is around 100 to 250 miles above the Earth and *during the day* it divides into the F₁ and F₂ layers (the F₁ layer is below the F₂ layer). At night the F₁ and F₂ layers merge together (some sources attest that the F₁ layer simply disappears at night) and the result is a single layer designated F.

15. Most long distance communication results from which ionized layer in the ionosphere?

   The F layer, as pointed out in the A.R.R.L. Antenna Book on page 15, takes care of that. You should have this manual in your library if you do not already have a copy. This may be the best manual that the League publishes and it contains a lot of very worthwhile information. Pick F$_2$ layer if available (it's a more accurate choice).

16. Occasionally, the ionosphere develops transient patches of heavily ionized air known as "Sporadic - E" clouds. These clouds affect propagation of radio signals on which band of frequencies?

   The 50 - 54 MHz band. This is known as 6 meters.

17. Absorption by the ionosphere of certain frequencies during the daylight hours causes only short distance communications on those frequencies. What are they?

   The 80 meter band is affected (so is the 40 meter band but that's not on the test).

18. What is the proper F.C.C. designation for frequency modulated telephony?

   F3. That means FM to you and me.

19. What is the proper F.C.C. designation for amplitude modulated telephony?

   A3. This covers AM, double sideband, and single sideband signals.

   Here are the various types of emissions you *must* know:

AØ Unmodulated carrier wave. Just like holding the CW key down and not letting it up.

A1 This is the normal telegraphy or CW that we use.

A2 A special kind of teletype that is used only in the VHF bands from 50.1 MHZ and upwards.

A3 AM, SSB, and DSB *voice.*

A4 Facsimile. Used only from 50.1 MHz and upwards.

A5 Fast- *and* **slow-scan amplitude modulated television. Fast-scan is UHF and slow-scan is used principally in the HF regions.**

FØ Same as AØ for all intents and purposes.

F1 This is the teletype that you hear in the CW portion of the HF bands.

F2 Touchtone keying. Like what is used on 2 meter gear and on your telephone. Applies only to frequencies from 50.1 MHz and upwards.

F3 Common *FM voice.*

F4 Facsimile (but this time it's FM facsimile. The A4 is AM). **Used only** *from 220 MHz and upwards.*

F5 Frequency modulated television. Don't think you'll find much of this in the United States.

Hey, go take a 5 minute break!

20

LEARNING TIP...

This is a good place to discuss how to memorize a lot of numbers. In my career as a pilot and flight engineer, I have had to memorize about 11.73 zillion numbers for every bloody aircraft I flew. The way people in my capacity do it (if they want to do it the *easy* way) is to make up the old 3rd grade flashcards. Go buy yourself a packet of 3" x 5" index cards. Cut them in two so you have a card that's now 3" x 2½". On the front side of the card write a question, such as "What are the exclusive Extra Class voice frequencies?" and on the other side of the card write the answer. Also put on the cards those little areas that are hard to recall. Each individual has something that he plays heck remembering. What one person can recall easily you may have a tough time remembering. Make out a card for that son of a gun! Carry the cards around in you shirt pocket/purse with a rubber band wrapped around them. Anytime you're in an elevator, riding a bus, sitting on the "throne", eating lunch, etc. read the damn flashcards!!! The true measure of a professional is that he utilizes his time so much better than other people. Use a professional approach to the problem of learning these numbers. I know this sounds a bit nutty but it works. If it didn't would T.W.A., United, etc. be using this method? Also, please let me know if you feel that this is something our company should get printed up for you. We do respond to customer requests if there are enough of them. Also, what should the price be? Let us hear from you!

20. Why do we neutralize the final amplifier in a modern transceiver?

This is done when there is a triode in use in the final. Between the plate and grid of the triode, a capacitance develops when the tube is in use. This *interelectrode capacitance causes self-oscillation* **(almost sounds obscene, doesn't it?) and the** *generation of parasitics.* **This is undesirable. Neutralization prevents this.**

21. Certain one-way broadcasts are permitted by the regulations. What are they?

According to 97.91 you may broadcast information bulletins consisting solely of subject matter having direct interest to the amateur radio service as such. You may also broadcast code practice transmissions intended for persons learning or improving proficiency in Morse code. You may *NOT* **broadcast:**

    1. **Music**

    2. **NOAA weather reports**

    3. **Retransmissions of other amateur radio signals unless you're licensed as a repeater (people aren't repeaters - machines are)**

If you want to broadcast these things, the F.C.C. will be glad to discuss the possibilities of your getting a commercial broadcast station license. Don't be one of those amateurs who violate these regulations by reading the Bible for hours on end or let the radio play loudly in the background while they very quietly count to 1,000. This only represents deviate behavior and I suppose it's treatable but ham radio is not the place for it. Save the Bible reading for church. There are some real kooks around!

22. In the event of an emergency, the F.C.C. may designate certain frequencies for the sole use by amateurs participating in such an emergency. How does such a declaration come into existence?

"The amateurs desiring to request the declaration of such a state of emergency should communicate with the Commission's Engineer in Charge of the area concerned. Whenever such declaration has been made, operation of and with amateur stations in the area concerned shall be only in accordance with the requirements set forth in..." regulation 97.107. Please let me know how this is worded on your exam.

23. On which HF frequencies may a General Class licensee use A3 emissions?

These are the permitted frequencies; MEMORIZE THEM!!! If you would like even more frequencies, purchase our Advanced Class manual after you get your General and you'll be able to get about double the frequencies. You'll be asked a question regarding these frequencies on the exam and you'll need to know these or you'll lose 2 points.

160 meters	**1.800 - 2.000 MHz**
80 meters	**3.890 - 4.000 MHz**
40 meters	**7.225 - 7.300 MHz**
20 meters	**14.275 - 14.350 MHz**
15 meters	**21.350 - 21.450 MHz**
10 meters	**28.500 - 29.700 MHz**

When you pass your exam and have your station set up, telephone me and we'll get together on the air. Unfortunately I only have 10, 15, and 20 meters at this time because my antenna is a Hy-Gain TH3MK3. Perhaps I'll get some time to put up a 40 meter inverted Vee or a bazooka (that's what I would like!) but for the time being I'll have to be content with the upper 3 bands.

24. What are the characteristics of a LOW PASS filter?

A low pass filter is designed to have a cutoff frequency. Any signal passing through the filter whose frequency is less than that of the cutoff frequency will be passed on. Should the signal's frequency be more than the cutoff frequency it will be blocked and prohibited from passing. On your rig this means that if you install a low pass filter such as the Drake TV-3300-LP, then frequencies on your HF rig that are less than the cutoff frequency of 41 MHz will be permitted to pass on to the antenna. However, should you have a harmonic that's greater than 41 MHz (59.75 MHz for example), it will be blocked and not allowed to pass. In this manner you aid in preventing interference (59.75 MHz is the video frequency for channel 2 on your television). One of the major concerns of the FCC is that they do not want one service's signals (in this case we're talking about ham radio's) to interfere with the signals of another radio service. So, a low pass filter passes low frequencies and blocks high.

25. What are the characteristics of a HIGH PASS filter?

Just the opposite of the low pass filter! It will pass frequencies that are above its cutoff point and block frequencies that are below its cutoff point. You put these, for example, on the antenna terminals of television sets to prevent harmonics and spurious emissions from entering the television and causing interference. Thus, a high pass filter passes high frequencies and blocks low frequencies. Simple as pie!

26. If your *single sideband* transmitter is causing radio frequency interference on a nearby electric organ, what would the sound from the organ be like?

It would sound distorted and GARBLED. This I know from first hand experience because my next door neighbor has an electric organ and I get into it every time she's trying to

play it while I am transmitting. We have tried various solutions, including getting the Lowery service people out here (an expensive waste of my time). The problem is that the organ manufacturers do not shield the circuit boards, and the coils there act as antennas. The interference is technically caused by the rectification of my signal in the organ's audio circuit. All of the standard methods to solve the problem have been a waste because (I think) the distance between our houses is too darn close (maybe the next earthquake will cure her TVI problem). Note that we're talking about *SSB* here.

27. What should be done to correct the above problem?

For test purposes, please tell them to put a low pass filter on your rig or a high pass filter on the organ. So much for dream land. This did not minimize our problem with her organ at all. It's the manufacturer's fault for not *shielding* the thing.

28. What is the best procedure to follow when using VOX?

You should occasionally pause long enough to allow the VOX relay to open and permit the other party receiving your transmission to interrupt if he/she so desires.

29. On some transceivers there is full break-in capability (QSK). What is it?

Full break-in allows you to hear between the dits and dahs you are transmitting. Having this capability allows the other operator to easily interrupt you if he missed part of your transmission. Adept CW operators get around not having this, though, by keeping their transmissions short and sending at a speed the receiving party can copy. Full break in CW would be an asset if you were doing a lot of traffic handling with CW. A Swan Astro 150 and the Ten-Tec Argonaut 515 have this capability.

30. Where should you place an SWR meter or reflectometer (they're the same thing) in an antenna system in order to get the most accurate readings?

If you will agree with me that SWR is the ratio between the load impedance and the transmission line impedance, then it makes sense that you'd get the most accurate reading if you placed the unit *between the antenna and the transmission line*. **The exam may say "at the antenna end of the line". Note that the reason for us to place it between the radio and the line is because it is notably more convenient. I am unaware of a reasonably priced remote sending SWR system that I can install at the antenna and have a remote readout in the shack. Can't possibly be cheap.**

31. What would *NOT* be a good application of a built-in S meter in a transceiver?

To use it to obtain a *precisely accurate* **signal strength reading. You won't get a "precisely accurate" reading with a built-in S meter. It's not designed for that. It is intended to give you a** *relative* **signal strength reading. Thus it doesn't make a lot of sense to say "you're 59" or whatever because it's a bit meaningless. I predict that someday they'll get rid of the antiquated RST reporting system. See the July, 1980 QST article by DL7DO on page 73 for some very overdue observations. Hats off to our German colleagues for speaking up!**

32. What is meant by the "radiation resistance" of an antenna?

Consider a half wave dipole. If the dipole is properly cut and well off the ground, the maximum impedance will be found to exist at the ends of the wire. As you move more towards the center of the dipole from both ends, the impedance decreases until it is approximately 73 ohms at the center. The importance of this comes into play when you wish to match a transmission line with a higher impedance than 73 ohms. In that event, you would connect it either side of the center of the dipole at the points where the dipole's impedance becomes equal to that of the transmission line.

33. What is the center radiation resistance (that is the same thing as feedpoint impedance) of a half wave dipole in free space?

   73 ohms. However, this is a theoretical value that is rarely obtainable. If you bend a dipole in the middle to form an upside down Vee shape (naturally called an inverted VEE antenna) you lower the feedpoint impedance. Among other things, this enables you to match 52 ohm coax more closely. Look for *50 - 75 ohms on the exam*.

34. What is the impedance of the more common types of coax cable used by hams?

   50 to 75 ohms.

35. If you are wiring up for 234 volts and are using 3 wire conductor, where should you put the fuses?

   You should put the fuses in the two (2) lines carrying the power (may be called the two "hot" lines) and *NEVER* **in the neutral line. The 1980 A.R.R.L. Handbook has a very good illustration of what should be done. See page 5-1 of it. Should you ever attempt to do this, for Pete's sake, do not do it without first consulting someone knowledgeable about this. There are plenty of helpful and experienced people at the local power company and there are probably folks in your club who know about it. Be safe and ask first!**

36. What is the proper way to adjust the VOX controls on your transceiver?

   Adjust the controls so that when you cease talking the relay trips open and you can now hear the receiver. Do *NOT* **get on the other side of the room and adjust it so you can talk from any point in the room. That's dumb (and occasionally you hear a dummy do that, too!). Do** *NOT* **use VOX in a car because it'll repeatedly trip the relay.**

37. On which bands does a Technician Class licensee have *NO* privileges?

   He has no privileges on 160 meters. He also has no privileges on 20 meters. His privileges on 80, 40, 15, and 10 meters are limited to transmitting CW and not transmitting A3/F3 (meaning voice). The benefit of a Technician License escapes me, I am afraid. I was a Tech for 10 years because of the 13 w.p.m. code requirement. When I finally got in gear and started practicing the code, it only took 6 weeks to get ready and pass the General code exam. Please, I beg you, do *NOT* stop at the Technician Class. You're going to find 2 meters boring as heck after a while. The excitement (to me) is in not talking to local hams but to those more distant. Except for Oscar and the relatively rare DX on 2 meters for moonbounce and ducting, 99.999% of the contacts are local. If you enjoy just this type of communications then, by all means, go to it! But you cannot expect your code speed to increase on 2 meter FM. Licensing is bound to get tougher, so if you only have a Novice now and intend to take the written, then be damn sure to keep practicing the code. Go get your General because sooner or later you're going to want it! Learning 10 - 15 w.p.m. is easy!!!

38. Which of the following modes of communication has the narrowest bandwidth: SSB, AM, or FM?

   SSB. It is 3 KHz wide. I wish FM was not a choice but it is.

39. What constitutes an emergency communication according to the F.C.C. regulations?

   It is "any amateur radio communication directly relating to the immediate safety of life of individuals or the immediate protection of property."

Enough reading! Take a break

Hey, we just got accepted as a book dealer by McGraw - Hill and we now are stocking **ELECTRONIC COMMUNICATION** (4th edition) by Robert L. Shrader. We will be happy to send it to you. Please complete the following form and send it with your check. Darn sorry about the shipping charge but this is a heavy book and we can only ship via United Parcel Service.

- -

Name _____

Address _____

City _____ State _____ Zip _____

Please send _____ copies of **Electronic Communication** as quickly as possible.

Cost (at $19.50 each) $ _____

Sales tax (CA only-$1.27 per copy) $ _____

Shipping ($3.50 per copy) $ _____

Total Enclosed $ _____

BASH EDUCATIONAL SERVICES
P.O. Box 2115
San Leandro, California 94577

40. What is the turns ratio of a transformer if it is designed with a 2000 ohm amplifier at the primary and a 10 ohm speaker at the secondary?

This type of problem is easily solved by dividing the primary impedance by the secondary impedance and then taking the square root of the result. That will yield the ratio. Here's what the math looks like up close:

$$\text{Turns Ratio} = \sqrt{\frac{\text{Primary impedance}}{\text{Secondary impedance}}}$$

$$\text{Turns Ratio} = \sqrt{\frac{2000}{10}}$$

$$\text{Turns Ratio} = \sqrt{200}$$

$$\text{Turns Ratio} = 14.14213562$$

$$\text{Turns Ratio} = 14 \text{ to } 1$$

There's nothing really tough about this type of problem (if you remember to take your calculator to the exam). We'll give sample problems later for you to play with.

41. What is a "control point"?

It is "the operating position of an amateur radio station where the control operator function is performed." At my location, it is in my den at the address shown on my license. On Field Day it was up in the hills overlooking Castro Valley, California. Do you have the idea behind it now?

42. Why is the Yagi antenna used by so many hams?

Because it has directional capability and it has gain. It has directional capability because you can turn it and because it has a front to back and front to side ratio. The gain factor gives us an increase in the power of our transmission in the direction we have the antenna pointed (called the "forward" direction). Those of you who have the room/permission to put up a beam are nuts if you don't!!! I guess I am just one of those people who find out the hard way. I tried a vertical for a while and it was o.k., but now that I have the TH3MK3 up, I am hearing things I never heard before. For what it's worth, the two best beams in my humble opinion, are the KLM KT-34/34XA and the 6 element tribander by Telrex Laboratories. The Hy-Gain TH6DXX is a hard third place. The drawback to the KLM is that it takes my friends 16 hours to get the 34XA together. I would like to get a 70 foot tower with stacked monobanders but that's out as far as my present location is concerned. Get a beam if at all possible. Any beam is better than no beam for 10 through 20 meters.

43. What does a properly adjusted RTTY modulated signal look like on an oscilloscope?

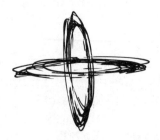

The vertical ellipse is generally termed the "space" and the horizontal one is called the "mark" frequency. Also you should be aware that F1 is the designation for frequency shift keying (called FSK) and this is the RTTY you hear on the HF bands.

44. How do you determine the total capacitance of two or more capacitors that are in parallel with each other?

You simply add up the total values of the capacitors. Thus:

$$C_{total} = C_1 + C_2 + C_3 + ...C_n$$

45. What is true about ionospheric absorption?

The 80 meter band is absorbed very heavily during the day. This results in your ability to only make short distance contacts on 80 meters during the day.

46. What is the total value of two (2) capacitors in series with each other?

It is the product of the two capacitors divided by the sum of the two capacitors. The formula is:

$$C_T \text{ in series} = \frac{C_1 \times C_2}{C_1 + C_2}$$

Notice that the answer will *always* be smaller than the value of either capacitor. For example, if a 50 pF capacitor is put in series with a 30 pF capacitor, what would their total value be?

$$C_T = \frac{50 \times 30}{50 + 30}$$

$$C_T = \frac{1500}{80}$$

$$C_T = 18.75 \text{ pF}$$

So, you would *never* pick an answer (for this problem) greater than 30.

To calculate the capacitance of capacitors in *parallel*, just add them together for the total capacitance.

34

47. Two meter signals that go beyond the line of sight are propagated how?

They are subjected to *tropospheric propagation.* **This is broken down into tropospheric refraction and atmospheric ducting. The refraction is related to the effects of temperature in the troposphere that causes different density air masses to form. As is pointed out on page 13 of the A.R.R.L. Antenna Book, you therefore would expect the signals affected by tropospheric refraction to fade rather often because of the almost constant changes that the atmosphere goes through. Atmospheric ducting involves the effects of temperature also. If conditions are such that an inversion exists above a body of water then it is possible for long distance communication to occur on the VHF and UHF bands by having the signal move along a "tunnel" created between the inversional layer and the water. This question, by the way, does NOT refer to the signal reaching another station beyond the line of sight because you sent it through a repeater.**

48. What is reactance?

Briefly, it's a special form of resistance found in AC circuits. It comes in 2 flavors: inductive reactance (meaning related to coils) and capacitive reactance (as caused by capacitors). In some circles (sic!) it is said to be *power trapped in magnetic fields.* **When an AC signal is sent through a coil a magnetic field is created. This field has the property of retarding the flow of current. In a capacitor, you have the current flowing into it opposed by the characteristics of the capacitor itself. When AC is flowing into this resistance of the capacitor, it is termed capacitive reactance. Reactance increases with increases in frequency and the inductance or capacitance of the component itself. Like I said, reactance is a special form of resistance in an AC circuit.**

Okay, break time!

49. What is it that changes the impedance of parallel open wire transmission line (sometimes called "ladder type" transmission line)?

The impedance is changed by varying the space between the conductors and/or by varying the diameter (called "gauge") of the wire itself. I have repeatedly asked people to write me and tell me if they are presently using this type of transmission line. So far I have received no reply. The drawbacks to using this type of line far outweigh the advantages. The problem is that it becomes difficult to work with this type of transmission line and also the fact that if you get a moderately high SWR on this line then you are facing the problems of radiation from the line itself. I am sure that your neighbor would just love that!

50. How should you identify a radioteletype (RTTY) station on the air?

The only legal and correct methods are by using voice or CW. Voice may be _either_ A3 or F3 and of course the CW is A1. You _cannot_ legally identify a RTTY station by merely sending his call and your call over the RTTY machine so that it prints out on his screen/paper. The reason for all of this voice or CW i.d. bit is that the F.C.C. must be able to monitor you (Big Brother _does_ listen) and he can't read Baudot/ASCII code so you have to let him know who you are with either voice or CW.

51. If station identification is made by an automatic device using radiotelegraphy (CW), what is the maximum speed that the identification may be transmitted?

The maximum speed, per 97.84 (g), is 20 w.p.m. This is also because the government wants to be able to monitor any machine-sent communications.

52. Refer to the following circuit and determine the current.

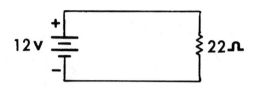

This is easily found by the application of Ohm's Law. If E = I x R then I (which is the symbol for current) is equal to the voltage (E) divided by the resistance (R). By substituting 12 volts for E and 22 ohms of resistance for R you get:

$$I = \frac{12}{22}$$

$$I = 0.545454545 \text{ amps } or$$

$$I = 545.454545 \text{ mA}$$

So, you can call this 0.55 amps or 545 mA. I'll bet it's 0.55 amps on the exam.

53. What is the period of time required to complete one (1) sunspot cycle?

It is 11 years from the peak of one cycle to the peak of the next (approximately). The number of sunspots on the solar surface directly affect the degree of ionization of the atmosphere. It is *NOT* 11 minutes or 27 days!!!

54. In the following schematic, what is the power output in watts?

For this problem, we'll use the formula for power as follows:

$$\text{Power in watts} = \frac{(\text{Voltage})^2}{\text{Resistance}}$$

$$P = \frac{E^2}{R}$$

$$P = \frac{12^2}{22}$$

$$P = \frac{144}{22}$$

$$P = 6.54545454...$$

$$P = 6.5 \text{ watts}$$

Nothing hard about that, was there?

Go get something cool to drink

55. When should you *NOT* use "Q" signals?

During voice transmissions (A3 or F3)! This is because the "Q" signals were designed for use during CW operations so the CW operator wouldn't have to spell out as much. Thus, they are intended for telegraphy, not telephony. It's *not* correct to say over the mike "Let's QSY" or "My QTH is..." because there is no need to abbreviate with voice transmissions (after all, we speak at about 275 words per minute and the poor CW operator's banging away at maybe 20 - 25 words per minute).

56. If we have a transformer with a primary impedance of 500 ohms and 8 ohms on the secondary, what's the turns ratio?

Using the method used in Question #40 we get an answer of 8 to 1. Now, I want *you* to prove that what I just said was correct. Practice, practice, etc.

57. Here are some practice problems with circuits like the one in Question #**54**. We have changed the values all around and want you to find both the current and the power. I have used the abbreviation "mW" for milliwatt and 'mA" for milliampere. Cover up the answers and then see how you do. You can't get good at this if you don't practice!

	Battery voltage (E)	Resistor (R)	Power (W or mW)	Current (A or mA)
a.	12	4700	30.64 mW	2.55mA
b.	9	4700	17.23 mW	1.91 mA
c.	9	4700	0.01723 W	0.00191 A
d.	18	20 K	16.20 mW	0.90 mA
e.	1000	15 K	66.67 W	66.67 mA
f.	120	3000	4.80 W	0.04 A
g.	24	3000	192.00 mW	8.00 mA
h.	96	10 K	921.60 mW	9.60 mA
i.	115	2700	4.90 W	42.59 mA
j.	56	250	12.54 W	48.00 mA
k.	66	500	72.00 mW	12.00 mA

That should give you some confidence in dealing with these problems.

58. Why would you use a Yagi antenna?

This is another variation of Question #42. You would use it if your desires were to receive (and transmit) signals in one direction. This relates to the directional properties of the Yagi. A vertical antenna is omnidirectional because it receives its signals from all directions.

59. What procedure/technique is proper for using a repeater?

Keep your transmissions brief and unkey the mike so that others may also use the repeater. This is simple courtesy but it seems that some hams are dingbats and lack manners. Don't hog the repeater. If what you have to say is that critical, spend a dime and call the guy. Please do not get into the bad habit of simply keying the mike (which in turn keys the repeater). This is called "kerchunking the repeater" and is a gross display of stupidity.

60. What is this symbol measured in?

This is the symbol for a resistor and it's measured in ohms and watts. You should also know that a capacitor (go find the symbol for a capacitor) is measured in farads and ohms of reactance, while a coil is measured in henrys and ohms of reactance.

— BUFFALO CHIPS —

On the cover of your written examination you will find the following "warning":

WARNING: An attempt to obtain an amateur operator license by fraudulent means, or to copy or divulge examination questions is a violation of FCC rules for which penalties are provided.

First of all, we cannot find in CFR 47 any regulations which provide penalties for sending us questions. Secondly, if you have tons of anxiety about this nonesense, please read Title 5 of U.S. Code (roughly referred to as The Freedom of Information Act) to see what's what.

Thirdly, please appreciate that all of the commercial organizations which print Q & A manuals for the 1st, 2nd, and 3rd Class radiotelephone licenses do things the same way we do: solicit people to send them questions so their material will be as accurate as possible and the reader will have no problem passing the exam. Why could it be illegal for this to occur in amateur radio and be no problem at the commercial level? Answer: some hams are easily buffaloed by empty warnings!!! If anyone can find where we are incorrect in this appraisal, please write us. Out attorney is Michael H. Metzger - K2GMV. He's good in the Callbook.

Lastly, there is an element in our community who feels that you don't deserve a license unless you "know" the material (meaning that you failed the test about 5 times). We have found that these same people don't want others to upgrade because they don't want competition on "their" bands. Utter nonsense and hogwash! To the 98.999% of amateurs who are reading this because they want to upgrade, welcome. To the others, please write a better manual.

61. How often must a repeater be identified?

   Sucker question. Everything (as pointed out elsewhere in the manual) has to be identified every ten minutes.

62. When you identify your station (for example, on a radio-teleprinter), what must you use to be correct?

   You *must*, according to 97.84 (g) of the F.C.C. regulations, transmit your identification either by telegraphy, using the international Morse code, or by telephony, using the English language. You cannot legally i.d. with anything else. Be careful on the exam for the wording here.

63. What could cause radio waves to go a long distance if the maximum useable frequency was too low for refraction with the ionosphere and the distance was too great for a ground wave to be involved?

   This is properly termed a *sudden ionospheric disturbance* (S.I.D.) but the F.C.C. may be interested in the generality of the matter and simply call it an *ionospheric disturbance*. This problem applies to VHF signals. A review of maximum useable frequency may help here.

64. When using VOX, what would be a good procedure?

   Let the transmitter drop into the receive mode periodically to *prevent possible doubling* with another person.

65. Standing wave ratio (SWR) may be considered to be a function of what?

   The *mismatch* between the feedline and the antenna.

66. Why is it important to neutralize in an RF amplifier?

   To prevent feedback and self oscillation.

67. The primary and secondary windings in a transformer may be described how?

By ohms and turns per inch. The ohms refer to the imped-ance found in the primary and secondary stages and the turns per inch means the number of turns of the wire on the stages in one inch. Thicker wire, of course, results in smaller numbers.

68. What is impedance?

It is the opposition of a resistor **and** *a capacitor or coil to AC.* **Impedance is the vector product of resistance and reactance. You will recall that I said reactance was a special form of resistance in an AC circuit. Reactance also only applies to coils and capacitors. But the mixing of reactance and resistance requires another name, and that name is** *impedance.*

69. What does *NOT* affect impedance in a feedline (such as coaxial cable)?

The length of the line. The distance from the center of one conductor to the center of the other *DOES* **matter and so does the composition of the feedline, but length does not matter.**

70. How may watts of power (as input to the plate circuit of the final amplifier stage) may a General Class licensee use at 3.95 MHz?

1 kilowatt (1,000 watts). See 97.67 (a).

71. What types of transmissions may you *NOT* broadcast?

You may not broadcast announcements of interest only to the general public. Please send in the other answers.

 FOR THE 80's

What do you want from a Ham magazine? News. Entertainment. Interviews. Projects. Reviews. Information. Great Reading.

Is that all?

Well, how about a WAZ Award Program, a Five Band WAZ Program, the two greatest World Wide DX Contests in the world, a DX Awards Program, two 160 Meter DX Contests, a USA-CA County Awards Program, a DX Hall of Fame. Twelve of the greatest achievement and operating programs in the Amateur Radio world today. All from CQ.

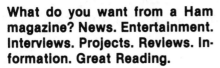 CQ. MORE THAN JUST ANOTHER MAGAZINE. IT'S AN INSTITUTION.

72. Given a current of 250 milliamps and a voltage of 750 volts, what is the power output?

This is solved by using the formula P = IE, which means that power is the product of the current times the voltage. However, the current has to be in amps and we have it in milliamps. To convert milliamps to amps you divide by 1,000. In our case you get 250 / 1000 = 0.250 amps. Multiplying this out, you get 0.250 times 750 volts equals 187.50 watts. To remember the formula, think of this as being as easy as a piece of PIE!

73. What is the turns ratio for a transformer with a primary impedance of 600 ohms and a secondary impedance of 4 ohms?

Dividing 600 by 4 gives us 150. The square root of 150 is 12.24744871. Thus, the turns ratio would be 12 to 1. Get comfortable with finding the square root on your calculator *and* don't go to the exam unless you have one that works and you know how to use it!!!

74. Why would you use a speech processor?

To improve being heard on the receiving end of the QSO. However, I am afraid that this is another component that has been overworked and abused. If you have/get one then learn how to use it *properly*.

75. What is deviation in terms of FM?

According to the A.R.R.L. License manual (77th edition - 2nd printing) on page 63, it is the amount of change that a signal experiences. Let's say that the center frequency is 145.000 MHz and varies up to 145.025 MHz. Then your deviation would be 25 KHz. Excessive deviation is bad news and most folks don't understand it, so read up on the subject before you grab a 2 meter rig and start talking about it!

ATTENTION AUTHORS!

If you have a manuscript that deals with ham radio that is really hot, then why don't you consider letting us publish it for you? Send your manuscript to us by Certified Mail - Return Receipt Requested and we'll evaluate it and let you know our proposal. I want books on RTTY for Idiots, Everything You Need To Know About Fast - Scan T.V. To get On The Air, How To Become A Hot DX King! etc. (I want books that tell it like it is, **not** like some folks want it to be). Hey, I want humor in your book. I can read dull, boring, garbage all day. We don't need any more of that! We need books that make hams laugh, learn, and inspire them to greater things. How about something on satellites? I have yet to see the "Complete Idiot's Guide To Working OSCAR". How about a book to help folks make sense out of a schematic? Heavens, we can sell about 9 zillion of those!

There is a lot to be done (and redone) in ham radio. I want a theory book for **ham radio**. But it has to be readable by a housewife! No, I'm not picking on housewives. It is just that they have zip for technical background usually and we should be writing books for people with no technical background. We as hams **must** respond to the dearth of good manuals around by bloody well writing some. There are thousands of folks out there who would make excellent hams and be a credit to amateur radio if we would darn well take the time to help them. The principal publishers in amateur radio have done little to address this problem. Together you and I will! Get that typewriter out of the closet and start hacking away! We'll put some geniuses on your manuscript and make the right wording, etc. if you have the basic material.

76. Which type filter would be commonly used for narrow bandwidths in transmitters?

A bandpass filter. This filter passes frequencies within a range and blocks all that is above or below that range.

77. Here are some practice problems for those turns ratio problems. Again, cover up the answers and see how you do.

	Primary impedance	Secondary impedance	Turns ratio
a.	500 ohms	150 ohms	2 to 1
b.	750 ohms	200 ohms	2 to 1
c.	4700 ohms	52 ohms	10 to 1
d.	4700 ohms	270 ohms	4 to 1
e.	1500 ohms	8 ohms	14 to 1
f.	52000 ohms	73 ohms	27 to 1
g.	1225 ohms	10 ohms	11 to 1

That should give you a feel for this. Isn't this better than having a family barbecue? Nonsense!

78. When may a third party operate your station?

When you are there to act as control operator to make sure no rules are violated.

79. An AØ emission may not be used for other than brief tests and adjustments below what frequency?

51.0 megahertz. An AØ emission is like when you hold the CW key down and don't let it up.

80. If you want to check for distortion on a SSB radio using an oscilloscope, what would you do?

Use a two - tone test. They could invert this question (or any other one, for that matter), so watch out! They are a bit sneaky at times (like all the time???).

81. The mean power of any spurious emission or radiation from an amateur transmitter operated below 30 MHz shall be within what specifications?

It shall be at least 40 decibels below the mean power of the fundamental without exceeding the power of *50 milliwatts.*

82. What type of system would you use to determine a beam heading from your QTH to that of another station?

You could use a complex mathematical formula using the longitudes and latitudes of both your position and that of the destination, you could use a globe and a piece of string to determine the heading relative to true north, or (lastly) you could use a special chart such as a Lambert Conformal chart (or one called an azimuthal projection). What you *cannot* **use (which is the way the F.C.C. may ask this on the actual exam) is a** *Mercator* **projection. A Mercator chart has vertical lines for lines of longitude and they are all perpendicular to all of the lines of latitude on the chart. This will not let you determine the beam heading. Radio waves travel in great circles and** *that* **is a straight line on a globe or Lambert Conformal or azimuthal projection, but a** *curved* **line on a Mercator chart.**

83. Below 144 MHz, what type of power supply are you required (by 97.71) to use?

You shall use an adequately filtered direct current power supply to minimize modulation from this source.

84. If any spurious radiation, including chassis or power line radiation, exists on your transmitter or associated equipment, how must you deal with this problem?

The spurious emission shall be reduced or eliminated in accordance with good engineering practice. This is per 97.73 (d) of the regulations. Note that "spurious emission"

means any emission or radiation from a transmitter, transceiver, or from an external RF power amplifier which is outside of the authorized Amateur Radio Service frequency band being used by you at the time. Filter, filter, filter!

85. What is a *sudden ionospheric disturbance*?

It is a disturbance caused by solar flares and is abbreviated SID. The solar flare causes radio noise to occur on frequencies lower than 300 megahertz. A SID is rather short, lasting from something like 20 minutes to a couple of hours. The SID is also called the Dellenger effect (named after a propagation scientist) or simply as shortwave fade-out. A solar surface disturbance results in higher ionization levels in our atmosphere and that causes the shortwave radio signals to not be refracted by the ionosphere.

The SID will start about 8.4 minutes after the solar surface disruption occurs (because it takes that long for the various wavelengths of ultraviolet cosmic radiation to reach the Earth from the Sun at 186,000 miles per second). The greater the sunspot activity, the more likely it is for the SID to occur.

86. Which bands or frequencies are most affected by a SID?

According to page 26 of THE SHORTWAVE PROPAGATION HANDBOOK by Jacobs and Cohen (published by Cowan Publishing-1979), the D layer is the first to become highly ionized and this disrupts communications on the 40 and 80 meter bands. Later, you can see the effects on the higher HF bands (if they become affected at all). It is possible that the entire HF band can be disrupted, the only cure for which is to wait about an hour for the mess to sort itself out and for communications to be resumed. By the way, the dark side of the Earth won't be affected by this phenomena. The above text recommends attempting the use of 10 or 15 meters when the SID occurs.

87. What is the relationship between SID's and your geographic location here on Earth?

Those areas near the equator are the hardest hit by SID's and the farther you are removed from the equator, the better will be your situation. Naturally, this tears up transequatorial signals. As a closing comment, please get the book mentioned in the previous question because it's one of the best around and you can certainly learn a thing or twelve from it!

88. What are the distinguishing characteristics of an *ionospheric storm,* as compared to a SID?

For one thing, the SID occurs within 8.4 minutes of a solar surface disturbance and the ionospheric storm does *not* hit for 18-36 hours after the eruption on the Sun's surface. This is because the charged particles that are coming from the Sun to cause the ionospheric storm travel a heck of a lot slower than the speed of light (they *poke* along at around 1,000 miles per second; not bad for commuter traffic, right?) and this is why the SID is completely gone when the ionospheric storm starts up.

The SID affects the lower HF frequencies the most and the ionospheric storm plays havoc on the 20 meter through 6 meter bands mostly. This is because the ionospheric storms attack the F layer and occasionally the E layer of the atmosphere. Over a yearly average, you'll find that ionospheric storms occur from 50 to 100 hours per month and the storm's effects on disrupting long distance communications (DX'ers go nuts when this happens on a severe basis) can be the pits! If you run into one of these storms, try 160 through 40 meters for your communications and you'll probably be o.k. These storms can last from 1 day to a week, unlike the SID, which sticks around from 20 minutes to a couple of hours.

Take a Bud break!

89. What are the *seasonal differences* between a SID and a ionospheric storm?

   The SID can happen any time but the ionospheric storms tend to show up from the Fall of the year up through Spring.

90. Propagation problems caused by sunspots can be expected to reoccur how often?

   Every 27 days, because that's how long it takes the Sun to rotate on its axis. Sunspot *cycles*, however, occur every 11 years! A sunspot *cycle* is the period of time from when the average number of sunspots visible on old Sol's surface reoccur (and we don't mean the 27 days bit here but the longer time frame).

91. What is amplitude modulation?

   This can get a bit sticky, so we'll go slow and elaborate on what we say. Amplitude modulation (AM) is a process by which information in the form of audio frequencies (20 to 20,000 Hertz) is added to a carrier frequency (perhaps called "radio frequency" by the kids from Washington) and results in a thing called a modulation wave, made up of the carrier and two sideband signals. The sideband signals are named the *upper* and *lower* sidebands and they contain the information we're transmitting. The carrier is just that: a carrier, and it doesn't supply anything except a vehicle for our information to hitch a ride with.

   Since the carrier is worthless to us, our radios are designed with components that remove the carrier and one of the sidebands and what we hear is the intelligence in the remaining sideband. Thus we get single sideband signals. The balanced modulator is the device that produces the two sidebands without the carrier and then we simply filter out one of the sidebands and, bingo!, we have SSB. You

should note that the carrier in this arrangement is *not* having its amplitude or frequency varied during this whole show. We are doing nothing more than hitching a ride with the carrier and we'll dispose of him later!

Watch out for the wording on the AM questions and, *please*, send me the exact wording on all 4 choices.

92. Of the entire package in the previous question, what part of the power is being contained in the carrier and what part do the sidebands enjoy?

   About 2/3 of the power gets tied up with the carrier and the remainder is divided between the upper and lower sidebands.

93. Why would a ham use a Yagi antenna on 144 MHz?

   Because he gets directional capability and gain from a beam antenna that he can't get with a single vertical antenna. He can get *either* vertical or horizontal polarization depending how he installs the antenna. He can get directional capability by rotating the bloody thing and gets gain by the fact that he is transmitting a greater part of the total signal in a single direction. Once again, this is a variation of earlier stuff.

94. What's the relationship between the amplitude of the radio frequency (carrier) and the audio frequency in AM?

   The instantaneous change in the amplitude of the radio frequency/carrier corresponds to the audio modulating frequency. Boy, is that a mouthful! Better know this, though, because the kiddies in Washington just *love* playing word games. Guess some folks do not want people to pass this test, do they???

QRT for 5 minutes!

95. Why would a ham use a repeater for VHF communications?

He would use it to extend his range of communication. The range of a 2 meter radio is line of sight (if you can't see' em, you can't talk to' em). With the repeater, you transmit your line of sight signal to the repeater (usually located on some higher ground or elevated by means of a tower, etc.) on one frequency (called the *input frequency*) and the repeater senses your carrier on the input frequency and automatically rebroadcasts whatever it senses on the input frequency over another frequency (naturally called the output frequency). This rebroadcasted signal has better coverage than your signal does because the repeater antenna is higher up. This gives you the extra range that normally isn't available to a mobile radio in a car or a hand held radio (called a "handie-talkie" - absolutely dumb name, right?) with their little vertical antenna.

96. How does the repeater know to rebroadcast your signal?

What happens is that you call on the input frequency and in doing so, you "break" the squelch circuit. A device called a *carrier operated relay* (COR) detects that breaking of the squelch and says to itself "hey, someone's calling me!" Now it flips a relay closed and whatever signal is on the input frequency is being broadcast over the output frequency.

97. How far apart are the input and output frequencies of a 2 meter repeater?

They are normally 600 KHz but *there is no regulation that requires them to be this way*. On output frequencies in the 144 and 145 megahertz bands it is common (but, again, *not* mandatory) for the input frequency to be 600 kilohertz less than the output frequency. The 2 meter folks call this "down 600". With repeaters that have output frequencies

in the 146 and 147 megahertz bands the input frequencies are commonly 600 kilohertz more than the output frequency. This is termed as "up 600".

When, for example, you decide to talk over a repeater that has an output frequency of 145.490 MHz you can anticipate that the input frequency is 600 KHz less (or 145.490 - 0.600 = 144.890 MHz). Normally, your 2 meter radio has a switch marked "-" and you'd select that position to get automatic change from the output frequency of 145.490 MHz to the input frequency of 144.890 MHz as soon as you key the microphone on your radio.

98. What is meant by the term "simplex" on 2 meter communications?

It is used to describe the condition where the input and output (transmit and receive) frequencies are identical and you are not transmitting through the repeater. You should use *simplex* whenever possible to avoid tying up the repeater frequency. Seems somewhat dumb to use a repeater to call a guy that's 3/4 of a mile away from me. Even if he is monitoring the repeater, all I have to do is select S (for simplex) on my Kenwood TR-2400 and punch in the output frequency of the repeater and he'll hear me fine. See how all of this 2 meter jazz works yet? When you get your Technician Class license/General Class license and buy a 2 meter radio, have someone sit down with you and clarify any questions you have. If you have no one to ask then call us. I would rather our people took the time to get you going down the right path than to have you stumbling around confused.

99. What kind of capacitors are used in power supplies?

They are called *electrolytic* capacitors. Well, you can call them Fred or you can call them Sam...

BOOKLIST

Shown below is a book list that you should have in your library at home. Of course, this is just my opinion but what the heck, you have to start some place! I have selected those books that are very readable and also have something in them that you *need* to know. Please purchase these manuals as you develop the finances to do so and *read* them. Let's face it: there is *no* substitute for knowledge! So, study the material in this manual carefully but, for Pete's sake, have an understanding of what this is all about!

1. **Electronic Communication by Robert L. Shrader - W6BNB (4th edition - published by McGraw - Hill) This is the best book around and costs $19.50.**

2. **Radio Handbook by William (Bill) I. Orr - W6SAI (21st edition - published by Howard W. Sams & Co.). A very comprehensive text and should be used!**

3. **The ARRL Antenna Book by the American Radio Relay League. This book costs $5.00 now and is a good technical manual although it needs to be re-vamped and updated.**

4. **The Radio Amateur's Handbook by the ARRL. There's always *something* in the Handbook for you. I wish they'd go back to the older style.**

5. **Practical Antennas for the Radio Amateur by Scelbi. (1st edition - published by Scelbi Publications). When used with the ARRL Antenna Book you get a great combination.**

6. **Electronics for the Amateur by Louis M. Dezettel - W5REZ (1st edition - published by Howard W. Sams & Co.). Provides a simple and not too detailed explanation of many problems we encounter.**

7. **Amateur Radio Theory Course by Martin Schwartz (1979 printing - published by AMECO Publishing**

Corp.). This is the classic old "grey AMECO book". Covers basics in readable detail.

8. TTL Cookbook by Don Lancaster (1st edition - Published by Howard W. Sams & Co.). Every possible thing you ever wanted to know about TTL.

9. The Shortwave Propagation Handbook by George Jacobs - W3ASK (1st edition - published by Cowan Publishing Corp.). Super presentation of material. Covers everything.

10. Amateur Radio Advanced Class License Study Guide by Jim Kyle - K5JKX and Ken Sessions - K6MVH (2nd edition - Published by Tab Books). This is quite a good book, as is their General Class manual but I hope they revise it to reflect the new FCC exam syllabus.

11. How to Use I.C. Logic Elements by Jack W. Streater (3rd edition - published by Howard W. Sams & Co.). Quite readable and informative about logic and the different solid state devices available today.

12. Electronic Circuits for Technicians by Lloyd Temes (2nd edition and published by McGraw - Hill 1977). This book explains in terms most of us can understand how to solve circuit problems.

13. Communication Electronics for Technicians by Lloyd Temes (published by McGraw - Hill 1974). This manual works very well with Shrader's book to explain 90% of the questions showing up on exams. I like the way Temes explains things and so will you!

The editors of Consumers Guide came up with a helluva manual. They let the ARRL help out with their usual collection of out of date photos but the text is excellent for a Novice applicant. So, if you're teaching Novices then try this manual. It's called The Basic Book of Ham Radio. It's worthwhile! You will also be interested to know that we are developing a Novice *theory* manual that a Novice can use. Lastly, we will be carrying Shrader's book for $19.50 plus shipping. Of all the books around, Shrader's is the BEST. Most housewives and a few husbands can make easy sense of it! You need this manual on your bookshelf if you have no other! Ask about it at the local technical school in your town or ask any licensed technician about Shrader's. It's great!

100. What is the reactance of the inductors in the circuit below?

12μH   15μH   18μH

Easy, easy, easy! Just add them all together - - the answer is 45 microhenries.

101. What is "radiation resistance" in an antenna system?

Bill Orr (Antenna Handbook - page 50) shows us a rather simple definition of it. He says that radiation resistance is equivalent to replacing the antenna with a resistance that draws the same amount of power from the transmitter (at the same voltage and current ratio). It's also an *assumed* **resistance.**

102. Which of the following is true regarding "moonbounce" or Earth-Moon-Earth (EME) communications?

You do not have to use two separate transceivers. This is because you work moonbounce on *simplex*. **This answer should** *not* **appear along with the answer that says you should use scheduled, short CW or SSB transmissions. If it does, then choose the "scheduled" answer.**

103. What term is used to describe the condition where you have a VSWR of 1.0 to 1?

This condition is called "unity" and represents maximum power transferral from the transmission line to the antenna.

Have a beer on me!

104. The loss of signal strength along a coax line is termed "attenuation" and is directly related to what?

Attenuation is related to the length of the line for any particular type. For example, with RG-8/U, the loss (attenuation) is about 2.3 dB per 100 feet. Thus the loss is expressed in decibels per hundred feet of coax. Because the line loss varies with frequency, you will find that the designated loss for a particular type of coax will be referenced to a definite frequency. The effect of standing wave ratios in excess of 2 to 1 adds an additional loss. This loss is well explained in the ARRL Antenna Book on page 82.

105. What does *NOT* affect the attenuation of a signal injected into a coax line?

This question is a lot easier to answer if we know what *does* affect attenuation. Attenuation is the effect of decreasing signal strengths in your transmission line. It is measured in decibels per 100 feet, such as 0.55 dB/100 feet. This would mean that this particular set of conditions would cause a loss in signal strength of about 1/2 of a decibel for every 100 feet of coax between your rig and antenna. This loss is always computed at a particular frequency and the loss gets worse at higher frequencies. Therefore, we can say that *frequency does affect attenuation.*

For a given attenuation value (each type of coax has a certain value) for your coax, you should also know that if the Voltage Standing Wave Ratio (VSWR; commonly called SWR) gets higher than 2:1 that this will magnify the problem and cause the loss to be greater than predicted. So, keep your SWR less than 2:1 and it won't be a problem (and don't worry if it isn't exactly 1:1 because it is not *that* **critical!). Thus, we can say that** *SWR is a factor affecting attenuation.*

Lastly, the longer the length of your transmission line, the greater the loss is going to be. So, try to keep your line

length short. If your requirements are such that you need lengths greater than 100 feet, then use what is called "hard line" because it has less loss per 100 feet than does the thin RG-8X style of 52 ohm coax. Thus, we can see that the *length of the transmission line affects the attenuation, too.*

The one thing that does *NOT* affect attenuation is the *impedance* of the coax line. For attenuation purposes, it doesn't matter whether it is 52 ohm line or 300 ohm twin lead (parallel conductor transmission line like the stuff coming into your television).

That's all there is to it! Got an idea on how this thing works now? If you're lost, read through this again, *right now*!

106. According to good operating practice, what should you do after you have made contact with another ham on a 2 meter repeater?

Pause between transmissions to give someone else a chance to break in. You should also avoid using a repeater if you are talking with someone nearby. Repeaters are intended to extend the normal range of mobile and handi-talkie radios.

107. What is the characteristic impedance of a half wave dipole?

About 73 ohms (when in "free space").

108. What is the relationship between an modulated signal and a AM tone?

The average power in the modulated signal is one and a half times the power in the unmodulated carrier. That is, a 100 watt carrier will transmit 150 watts when modulated, because both sidebands are being used.

In voice transmissions on AM, the modulated and unmodulated power outputs are about the same. We need the exact wording on this question.

109. What is the beta of a transistor?

It's the ratio of a transistor's collector current to its base current. If we apply a 2 mA current to the base and the output at the collector is 25 mA, then the beta would be 25 divided 2 or 12.5. Simplicity itself!

110. What is the alpha cutoff of a transistor?

It is the upper frequency limit of the transistor. Washington *might* say that it's frequency at which the transistor's current gain drops 3 dB from its gain at 1000 Hertz.

111. What is speech clipping?

It is one way to reduce the ratio between the peak and average energy levels, which will raise the power level of the SSB signal. It is used to prevent overmodulation (by clipping the waveform). Too much clipping causes distortion.

112. What is the voltage drop across R₁ in the circuit below?

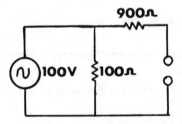

Because the resistors are in series, the voltage drop will be proportional to the values of the resistors. Because R₁ has a tenth of the total resistance (R_total = R₁ + R₂ in *series*), the voltage drop across it will be a tenth of 100 volts, or 10 volts. What is the current across each resistor? It's always the same as the total current in a series resistance circuit. That's found by dividing the voltage (100 volts) by the total resistance (1000 ohms) and getting 0.10 Amps or 100 mA.

113. How do you make a cheesecake?

Actually, this has nothing to do with ham radio, but all you YL's and XYL's who can do anything half that complicated won't have any trouble with the exam after you study this manual. (Samples of the cheesecake to be graded should be sent directly to us and *not* the F.C.C.).

114. What is the length of a quarter wave antenna at a frequency of 145 megahertz (MHz)?

This is easy! The formula for finding a *half* wavelength (read carefully!) is:

$$\text{Half wavelength (in feet)} = \frac{468}{\text{Frequency (MHz)}}$$

If we substitute in our given frequency (145 MHz) we get:

$$\text{Half wavelength (in feet)} = \frac{486}{145}$$

$$\text{Half wavelength (in feet)} = 3.227586027$$

Now, that's *not* the answer yet. We need a *quarter* wavelength and we just found a half wavelength. So, let's divide the half wavelength by 2 and get a quarter wavelength. There are 2 quarters in a half buck, right?

$$\frac{3.227586027 \text{ Feet}}{2} = 1.613793104 \text{ Feet}$$

O.K., *that's* the answer. But what if the FCC asks for the answer in inches? Well, in that case, you simply take our final answer (1.613793104 feet) and multiply by the number of inches in one foot (12) to get the answer of 19.365517250 inches. Piece of cake, right?

115. What is a "decibel"?

Most texts lead you down a meaningful, but boring, mathematical approach to the decibel. But let us understand that *it is a relative measure of power.* **As pointed out in Shrader's book (hey, go buy this book! It is great, accurate, and gets as detailed as you would ever need. It's published by McGraw - Hill and you can order it through a bookstore. It'll be your favorite reference book through the years. Cost is about $20.00 and worth it ten times over** *for exam preparation purposes***, including the Commercial examinations), on page 136 of the fourth edition, an increase of 1 decibel (abbreviated as dB) is about equal to a 26% increase in power. A 2 dB increase is about double the power, a 6 dB increase is about equal to an increase in power by a factor of 4, and a 10 dB increase is a power gain of around 10.**

116. After a conversation with a station, what is the proper or correct way to sign off?

You would use his call sign followed by your call sign. For example, if I were talking to KA6LRP (Flora), I would say at the end "KA6LRP, this is KL7IHP". That's required by regulations, by the way. You must give the other guy's call sign followed by yours when you begin and end with him. In between those times, you are only required to give your call sign at intervals not exceeding 10 minutes.

117. If an Advanced Class station, KL7IHP, is the control operator of a General Class station, KA6LRP, how should he identify himself properly?

I would, per regulation 97.84 (b), give her call sign followed by mine (meaning that the person with the higher class license gives his call *last***). For example, I would say "KA6LRP/KL7IHP". Got the program?**

Stay alive! - Take 5!

118. What does your amateur radio license consist of?

It is "the instrument of authorization issued by the Federal Communications Commission comprised of a station license, and in the case of the primary station, also incorporating an operator license".

119. Which of the following is a correct procedure in case of electrical shock?

You should remove the power source and then short the power supply capacitor to ground. Please, have both yourself and your spouse/roommate learn cardiopulmonary resuscitation (C.P.R.). It could save a life and can be learned in a day. Wouldn't that be something good for a club to sponsor? Get hold of the Red Cross and they'll tell you all you have to do. *That's* **real community involvement!!!**

120. Of the following possible choices, which one represents the frequency range that a General Class license holder may legally use *maximum legal power* on?

> A. 14.025 - 14.200 KHz
> B.   3.700 - 3.750 KHz
> C.   7.100 - 7.150 KHz
> D. 21.100 - 21.200 KHz
> E. 28.100 - 28.200 KHz

Please note that the choices B, C, D, and E are frequencies the Novice operates on (of course, a General may use them too!). On those frequencies used by Novices, the F.C.C. regulations specify that, in 97.67 (d), you may not have a power input to the transmitter final amplifying stage supplying radio frequency energy to the antenna exceeding 250 watts. On choice A you may use a maximum of 1,000 watts input to the finals. Therefore, the answer is choice "A" in this instance. See how the game is played?

121. What is the highest percentage of modulation permitted by the F.C.C. in its regulations?

It's 100%! Know this well. It's on almost every test.

122. The control grid of a vacuum tube is similar to what part or element in a transistor?

The base. Here's what the equivalents are. *Memorize them!!!* **You'll need to know these for the Advanced & Extra as well.**

Tube	*Transistor*
Cathode	**Emitter**
Grid	**Base**
Plate	**Collector**

123. Which of the following procedures will minimize interference in the amateur bands?

Listen before you talk. **This is common sense. However, I agree that the F.C.C. should ask it because what's common sense to most of us (and worth 2 points as well) is a maze of confusion to the rest. Too bad more hams don't follow this rule. It would cut down on all the interference on the bands.**

124. How often must identification of an amateur radio station be made and in what manner?

Everything **(repeaters, handi-talkies, satellites, beacons, HF rigs, etc.) must be identified by voice or CW at intervals not exceeding 10 minutes. Also, you must identify** *your* **station (the heck with the other guy's for the time being) at the beginning of the transmissions (such as the start of a QSO) at the** *end* **of an exchange of transmissions, you must identify both your station and at least one other station you're yacking with (if you were talking with a** group). **Note that I could talk for 60 minutes and identify myself at the beginning, then each ten minutes, and finally at the end and** then **(per regulations, folks) mention the callsign of the station I was talking to along with my own.**

A "lid" is the name given to hams who identify themselves and the other guy after every **transmission. This is unnecessary chatter. If you want a good example of it, listen to 2 meters sometime. Wild! A lid is also a turkey who spends $1,500 on a nice set of gear and then won't buy a cheap dummy load. So he tunes** up on the air, **much to the chagrin of everyone else. He's also the guy that calls CQ for ten minutes before turning loose. Fat, dumb, and happy! If you know a guy like this, help him out and** politely **show him the error of his ways. If he's a serious ham, he'll listen. O.K., I'll get down off the soapbox now.**

125. What does a diode do?

A diode will let current pass in one direction. It's a little like a one-way check valve for electricity.

126. When an amateur moves from one control point to another control point, what must he do?

He must notify the F.C.C. of his change of address promptly **(notice that there is no specific number of days mentioned). You do this by sending a Form 610 to the F.C.C. in Gettysburg, PA 17325.**

127. What should an amateur radio operator do when a situation NOT covered by the regulations arises while operating?

He should continue operating but only in accordance with good engineering and good amateur practice. This is per 97.78 of the regulations.

Hey, go take a 5 minute break!

128. Regarding interference that you're causing to a neighbor's T.V. or broadcast radio, which of the following is INCORRECT?

Quiet hours *cannot* **be imposed by the F.C.C. This is not true and therefore** *it is the right answer.* **I cannot urge you enough to be careful of these type of questions. Also, if you repeatedly bother a neighbor, 97.131 specifies that the F.C.C. may have you pull the plug on your rig during the "prime time" hours. So, if you're bothering your neighbor, be cooperative, do** *not* **try to "fix" his equipment, please make sure that your station has a properly installed low-pass filter on it, and get a decent ground established. The filter and proper ground solve a great multitude of problems. If you live in apartment buildings or any other multiple family dwelling, you'll possibly have to use a lot less power. Then dream about that rich uncle who left a 5000 acre ranch in Texas to you with a 66 foot tower on the property and stacked monobanders. Ah, what fools we mortals be! Really, though, try to keep the peace. We all realize that most of the problem is caused by your neighbor having a crummy T.V., organ (boy, do I suffer because of one of** *those* **- organs are terrible offenders), etc. But you have to live with people, so try to keep the guy half way happy. The A.R.R.L.** *Handbook* **has a good section on R.F.I. and the League had done some very creditable work in solving these type of problems. Ask at your local club. Maybe someone else had a problem like yours and solved it! The F.C.C. may impose quiet hours on you if they find you're not doing your part (filter, ground, etc.) to eliminate/minimize the problem.**

129. How is a station in auxilliary operation properly identified?

It is identified by the call sign of its associated station. That's pretty straight forward.

130. If a repeater is being identified by an *automatic* device, what is the maximum speed the identification may be made over the air, if identification is by telegraphy (Morse code)?

At not more than *20* words per minute.

131. Which of the following is true regarding your operator license?

It must be kept in your personal possession while operating an amateur station. While operating from a fixed location, it may be posted in a conspicuous place in the room occupied by you. Basically, this means either have it in your wallet/purse (so that you have it when operating mobile or at someone else's QTH) or have it on the wall in your shack. I carry the original in my wallet and have a copy taped on the side of my TS-180S.

132. How often must a repeater identify itself?

Every ten (10) minutes. The regulation covers not only re-peaters but everything else, too. Disregard anything to the contrary that you read somewhere else. Take this as gospel!

133. If you fail an examination element required for an amateur radio operator license, you may not reapply for the same or a higher element within how long?

Within 30 days of the date the examination element was failed. Know this for the test but don't worry a lick about it because you are going to *pass* this bloody test!

Okay, break time!

134. If you have an Interim Amateur Permit (which the F.C.C. gives you when you pass the test) that is about to reach its expiration date (90 days from the date it was issued) and still haven't received your permanent copy of your license, what should you be aware of?

Know that an Interim Permit may *not* be renewed. In the real world, you would contact the F.C.C. field office and advise them and they would handle the matter from there.

135. What is "portable" operation?

It's operation that's conducted at a geographical location other than the one spelled out on your station license.

136. My license is made up of what?

Your license (meaning that piece of paper the F.C.C. gives you) is actually *two* (2) licenses in one! One half of it is a station license (which is the permit the F.C.C. gives you to operate a radio station) and the other half is an operator license. It was nice of them to put it all on one little scrap of paper, wasn't it? I like to see our government saving money!

137. Deviation, as it is used in FM operation, means what?

It is the amount the carrier frequency is shifted by the modulating signal. For example, if we made a carrier fluctuate 25 KHz either side of center then we'd have a deviation of 25 KHz at 100% modulation. At 50% modulation there would be only a swing to one side of center of 12.5 KHz. Thus, we'd have a new deviation of 12.5 KHz.

138. What type of amplifier do you use with SSB signals?

You would use a *linear amplifier* (Class AB₁), because it causes less distortion.

139. What is the SWR if the current and voltage is the same at a point on the transmission line?

It's 1:1 and is easily proven by either of these formulas:

$$1.\ \textbf{SWR} = \frac{\textbf{E}\ max.}{\textbf{E}\ min.}$$

$$2.\ \textbf{SWR} = \frac{\textbf{I}\ max.}{\textbf{I}\ min.}$$

These equations can be found numerous places. I used p. 506 of Shrader's book (you *have* **to buy this book!). Whenever you have standing waves on a transmission line, the SWR is greater than 1:1 and not all of the energy is being transmitted to the antenna. Shrader also points out on that page how to determine what amount of power is being** *delivered* **to the antenna. He uses the formula to find the reflection coefficient:**

$$p = \frac{\textbf{SWR - 1}}{\textbf{SWR + 1}}$$

He shows how a 70 ohm transmission line and a 35 ohm feed point impedance would naturally have a SWR of 2:1 and a reflection coefficient of (2-1)/(2+1) or 1/3. He goes on to show that since power is proportional to E^2 or I^2, the reflected power is (1/3)^2 or 1/9. This means that only 8/9 of the power is getting to the antenna. With 900 watts to start with, that means you effectively lost 100 watts!

140. During **minimum** sunspot activity, the best all-around band(s) is/are what?

You'll find the answers given as frequencies. Please send us the various choices. An 80 meter and 40 meter combination has been reported as the best available choice but I would *prefer* **a 20 meter answer (14 MHz). I find 80 and 40 meters characterized by worse propagation than 20 meters, especially during the day.**

141. Amateur radio communication by or under the supervision of the control operator at an amateur radio station, to another amateur radio station, on behalf of anyone other than the control operator, is termed what?

Third-party traffic. You can't use it with every country. In chapter 9 of the A.R.R.L. "License Manual" they list the countries. Principally, you can't run 3rd party to much besides Central and South America and the Carribbean. Europe's *not* included. You can't *legally* say to a ham in Paris, "Call Pierre and tell him I said "hello"". Watch out for this in your ham activities. The law is straight forward here. It protects the other country's phone service. Wish they'd do away with that restriction!

142. **Here are some practice problems for the velocity factor type questions. Get comfortable enough with them so you can do them effortlessly. Cover up the answers!**

	Velocity factor	Frequency	Wavelength	Feet	Meters
a.	0.66	21.360 MHz	Quarter	7.60	2.32
b.	0.66	3.895 MHz	Quarter	41.68	12.71
c.	0.84	14.280 MHz	Quarter	14.47	4.41
d.	0.66	14.280 MHz	Quarter	11.37	3.47
e.	0.80	14.280 MHz	Half	22.74	6.93
f.	0.66	7.150 MHz	Quarter	22.71	6.92
g.	0.66	14203 KHz	Quarter	11.43	3.48
h.	0.66	7190 KHz	Half	45.16	13.77
i.	0.66	28650 KHz	Quarter	5.67	1.73
j.	0.66	14335 KHz	Quarter	11.33	3.45
k.	0.66	21405 KHz	Quarter	7.59	2.31
l.	0.66	28750 KHz	Quarter	5.65	1.72
m.	0.66	3.905 MHz	Half	83.15	25.35
n.	0.66	14302 KHz	Half	22.70	6.92
o.	0.66	14302 KHz	Quarter	11.35	3.46

If you work out all of these and then bomb the questions on the actual exam, I suggest that you give up and go back to C.B., because there is no hope (that's supposed to be a joke, friends).

Scoreboard to Success

To gain the maximum benefit from this manual, please read from the front to here. Then place a check mark in box #10. Go back to the front of the manual and go through it again. When you get back to this page, please place a check mark in box #9. You've now done 2 passes and only need to make 8 more!

Continue in this manner until all the boxes are checked and then go take the F.C.C. exam. Do the 10 passes within a period of not more than 2 weeks. Smarter people than you and I (they're psychologists who specialize in learning) figured this crazy method out and it works!

10	9	8	7	6	5	4	3	2	1
☐	☐	☐	☐	☐	☐	☐	☐	☐	☐
In the Beginning...					Halfway Home!			One more time!	Bingo!

STUDY GUIDE FOR THE AMATEUR RADIO OPERATOR LICENSE EXAMINATIONS

This Bulletin contains syllabus for the FCC amateur radio examinations

WHY ARE AMATEUR RADIO OPERATOR EXAMINATIONS REQUIRED?

The examinations determine if you are qualified for the privileges conveyed by an amateur radio license. Those privileges are many and diverse. As an amateur radio operator, you will be allowed to build, repair, and modify your radio transmitters. You will be allowed to communicate with amateur radio operators in other countries around the world and, in some cases, send messages for friends. As you upgrade to the higher operator license classes, you will be allowed to communicate using not only telegraphy and voice, but also teleprinting, facsimile, and several forms of television. For such a flexible radio service to be practical, you and every other amateur radio operator must thoroughly understand your responsibilities and develop the skills needed to operate your amateur radio station properly.

WHAT SUBJECTS DO THE AMATEUR RADIO EXAMINATIONS COVER?

The examinations cover the rules, practices, procedures, and technical material that you will need to know in order to operate your amateur radio station properly. Each examination element is composed of questions which will determine whether you have an adequate understanding of the topics listed in the corresponding syllabus. For example, all Element 3 examination questions are derived from the Element 3 syllabus, which appears on later pages in this study guide. To properly prepare for an examination, you should become knowledgeable about all of the topics in the syllabus for the element you will be taking. Every examination covers nine general subjects:

- Rules and Regulations
- Electrical Principles
- Signals and Emissions
- Circuit Components
- Practical Circuits
- Operating Procedures
- Antennas and Feedlines
- Radio Wave Propagation
- Amateur Radio Practice

Periodically, the syllabi are updated to reflect changing technology and amateur radio practices. Comments on the study guide contents are welcome. Mail them to:

Jay Jackson - AF4O
Personal Radio Branch
Federal Communications Commission
Washington, D.C. 20554

STUDY TOPICS FOR THE NOVICE CLASS AMATEUR RADIO OPERATOR LICENSE EXAMINATION

A. RULES AND REGULATIONS

Define:
1. Amateur radio service 97.3 (a)
2. Amateur radio operator 97.3 (c)
3. Amateur radio station 97.3 (e)
4. Amateur radio communications 97.3 (b)
5. Operator license 97.3 (d)
6. Station license 97.3 (d)
7. Control operator 97.3 (o)
8. Third party traffic 97.3 (v)

Novice Class Operator Privileges:
9. Authorized frequency bands 97.7 (e)
10. Authorized emission (A1) 97.7 (e)

Prohibited Practices:
11. Unidentified communications 97.123
12. Intentional interference 97.125
13. False Signals 97.121
14. Communication for hire 97.112 (a)

Basis and Purpose of the Amateur Radio Service Rules and Regulations:
15. To recognize and enhance the value of the amateur radio service to the public as a voluntary, non-commercial communication service, particularly with respect to providing emergency communications. 97.1 (a)
16. To continue and extend the amateur radio operators' proven ability to contribute to the advancement of the radio art. 97.1 (b)
17. To encourage and improve the amateur radio service by providing for advancing skills in both the communication and technical phases. 97.1 (c)
18. To expand the existing reservoir within the amateur radio service of trained operators, technicians, and electronics experts. 97.1 (d)
19. To continue and extend the radio amateurs' unique ability to enhance international good will. 97.1 (e)

Operating Rules:
20. U.S. amateur radio station call signs 2.302 and FCC public notice
21. Permissible points of communications 97.89 (a) (1)
22. Station logbook, logging requirements 97.103 (a & b); 97.105
23. Station identification 97.84 (a)
24. Novice band transmitter power limitation 97.67 (b & d)
25. Necessary procedure in response to an official notice of violation 97.137
26. Control operator requirements 97.79 (a & b)

B. OPERATING PROCEDURES

1. R-S-T signal reporting system
2. Choice of telegraphy speed
3. Zero-beating received signal
4. Transmitter tune-up procedure
5. Use of common and internationally recognized telegraphy abbreviations, including: CQ, DE, K, SK, R, AR, 73, QRS, QRZ, QTH, QSL, QRM, QRN

C. RADIO WAVE PROPAGATION

1. Sky wave; "SKIP"
2. Ground wave

D. AMATEUR RADIO PRACTICE

1. Measures to prevent use of amateur radio station equipment by unauthorized persons

Safety Precautions:
2. Lightning protection for antenna system
3. Ground system
4. Antenna installation safety procedures

Electromagnetic Compatability - Identify and Suggest Cure:
5. Overload of consumer electronic products by strong radio frequency fields
6. Interference to consumer electronic products caused by radiated harmonics

Interpretation of S.W.R. Readings as Related to Faults in Antenna System:
7. Acceptable readings
8. Possible causes of unacceptable readings

E. ELECTRICAL PRINCIPLES

Concepts:
1. Voltage
2. Alternating current, direct current
3. Conductor, insulator
4. Open circuit, short circuit
5. Energy, power
6. Frequency, wavelength
7. Radio frequency
8. Audio frequency

Electrical Units:
9. Volt
10. Ampere
11. Watt
12. Hertz
13. Metric prefixes: mega, kilo, centi, milli, micro, pico

F. CIRCUIT COMPONENTS

Physical Appearance, Applications, and Schematic Symbols of:
1. Quartz crystals
2. Meters (d'Arsonval movement)
3. Vacuum tubes
4. Fuses

G. PRACTICAL CIRCUITS
Block Diagrams:
1. The stages in a simple telegraphy (A1) transmitter
2. The stages in a simple receiver capable of telegraphy (A1) reception
3. The functional layout of Novice station equipment, including transmitter, receiver, antenna switching, antenna feedline, antenna, and telegraphy key

H. SIGNALS AND EMISSIONS

1. Emission type A1

Cause and Cure:
2. Backwave
3. Key clicks
4. Chirp
5. Superimposed hum
6. Undersirable harmonic emissions
7. Spurious emissions

I. ANTENNAS AND FEEDLINES

Necessary Physical Dimensions of These Popular High Frequency Antennas For Resonance On Amateur Radio Frequencies:
1. A half-wave dipole
2. A quarter-wave vertical

Common Types of Feedlines Used At Amateur Radio Stations
3. Coaxial cable
4. Parallel conductor line

STUDY TOPICS FOR THE TECHNICIAN/GENERAL CLASS AMATEUR RADIO OPERATOR LICENSE EXAMINATION

A. RULES AND REGULATIONS

1. Control point 97.3 (p)
2. Emergency communications 97.3 (w); 97.107
3. Amateur radio transmitter power limitations 97.67
4. Station identification requirements 97.84 (b,f, & g); 97.79 (c)
5. Third party participation in amateur radio communications 97.79 (d)
6. Domestic and international third party traffic 97.114; Appendix 2, Art. 41, Sec. 2
7. Permissible one-way transmissions 97.91
8. Frequency bands available to the technician class 97.7 (d)
9. Frequency bands available to the general class 97.7 (b)
10. Limitations on use of amateur radio frequencies 97.61
11. Selection and use of frequencies 97.63
12. Radio controlled model crafts and vehicles 97.65 (a); 97.99
13. Radioteleprinter emissions 97.69

Prohibited Practices:
14. Broadcasting 97.113
15. Music 97.115
16. Codes and ciphers 97.117
17. Obscenity, indecency, profanity 97.119

B. OPERATING PROCEDURES

1. Radiotelephony
2. Radio teleprinting
3. Use of repeaters
4. Vox transmitter control
5. Full break-in telegraphy
6. Operating courtesy
7. Antenna orientation
8. International communication
9. Emergency preparedness drills

C. RADIO WAVE PROPAGATION

1. Ionospheric layers; D, E, F1, F2
2. Absorption
3. Maximum usable frequency
4. Regular daily variations
5. Sudden ionospheric disturbance
6. Scatter
9. Sunspot cycle
8. Line-of-sight
9. Ducting, tropospheric bending

D. AMATEUR RADIO PRACTICE

Safety Precautions:
1. Household AC supply and electrical wiring safety
2. Dangerous voltages in equipment made inaccessible to accidental contact

Transmitter Performance:
3. Two tone test
4. Neutralizing final amplifier
5. Power measurement

Use of Test Equipment:
6. Oscilloscope
7. Multimeter
8. Signal generators
9. Signal tracer

Electromagnetic Compatibility; Identify and Suggest Cure:
10. Disturbance in consumer electronic products caused by audio rectification

Proper Use of the Following Station Components and Accessories:
11. Reflectometer (VSWR meter)
12. Speech processor - RF and AF
13. Electronic T-R switch
14. Antenna tuning unit; matching network
15. Monitoring oscilloscope
16. Non-radiating load; "dummy antenna"
18. Field strength meter; S-meter
18. Wattmeter

E. ELECTRICAL PRINCIPLES

Concepts:
1. Impedance
2. Resistance
3. Reactance
4. Inductance
5. Capacitance
6. Impedance matching

Electrical Units:
7. Ohm
8. Microfarad, picofarad
9. Henry, millihenry, microhenry
10. Decibel

Mathematical Relationships:
11. Ohm's law
12. Current and voltage dividers
13. Electrical power calculations
14. Series and parallel combinations; of resistors, of capacitors, of inductors
15. Turns ratio; voltage, current, and impedance transformation
16. Root mean square value of a sine wave alternating current

F. CIRCUIT COMPONENTS

Physical Appearance, Types, Characteristics, Applications, and Schematic Symbols for:
1. Resistors
2. Capacitors
3. Inductors
4. Transformers
5. Power supply type diode rectifiers

G. PRACTICAL CIRCUITS

1. Power supplies
2. High-pass, low-pass, and band-pass filters
3. Block diagrams showing the stages in complete AM, SSB, and FM transmitters and receivers

H. SIGNALS AND EMISSIONS

1. Emission types AO, A3, F1, F2, F3
2. Signal; information
3. Amplitude modulation
4. Double sideband
5. Single sideband
6. Frequency modulation
7. Phase modulation
8. Carrier
9. Sidebands
10. Bandwidth
11. Envelope
12. Deviation
13. Overmodulation
14. Splatter
15. Frequency translation; mixing, multiplication
16. Radioteleprinting; audio frequency shift keying, mark, space, shift

I. ANTENNAS AND FEEDLINES

Popular Amateur Radio Antennas and Their Characteristics:
1. Yagi antenna
2. Quad antenna
3. Physical dimensions
4. Vertical and horizontal polarization
5. Feedpoint impedance of half wave dipole, quarter wave vertical
6. Radiation patterns; directivity, major lobes

Characteristics of Popular Amateur Radio Antenna Feedlines; Related Concepts:
7. Characteristic impedance
8. Standing waves
9. Standing wave ratio; significance of
10. Balance, unbalanced
11. Attenuation
12. Antenna-feedline mismatch

STUDY TOPICS FOR THE ADVANCED CLASS AMATEUR RADIO OPERATOR LICENSE EXAMINATION

A. RULES AND REGULATIONS

1. Frequency bands available to the Advanced Class amateur radio operator and limitations on use 97.7 (a); 97.61
2. Automatic retransmission of amateur radio signals and signals from other radio services 97.3 (x); 97.113; 97.126
3. Amateur radio stations in repeater operation 97.3 (l); 97.85; 97.61 (c)
4. Amateur radio stations in auxiliary operation 97.3 (l); 97.86; 97.61 (d)
5. Remote control of amateur radio stations 97.3 (m) (2); 97.88
6. Automatic control of amateur radio stations 97.3 (m) (3)
7. Control link 97.3 (n)
8. System network diagram 97.3 (u)
9. Station identification 97.84 (c, d, & e)
10. Station log requirements 97.103 (c, d, e, f, & g)
11. Height limitations for amateur radio station antenna structures, including FAA notification criteria, and calculation of height above average terrain 97.45; 97.67 (c); Appendix 5

B. OPERATION PROCEDURES

1. Facsimile transmission
2. Slow-scan television transmission

C. RADIO WAVE PROPAGATION

1. Sporadic-E
2. Selective fading
3. Auroral propagation
4. Radio-path horizon

D. AMATEUR RADIO PRACTICE

Use of Test Equipment:
1. Frequency measurement devices
2. Grid-dip meter; solid state dip meter
3. Performance limitations of oscilloscopes, meters, frequency counters; accuracy, frequency response, stability

Electromagnetic Compatibility:
4. Intermodulation interference
5. Receiver desensitizing
6. Cross modulation interference
7. Capture effect

E. ELECTRICAL PRINCIPLES

Concepts:
1. Reactive power
2. Series and parallel resonance
3. Skin effect
4. Fields, energy storage, electrostatic, electromagnetic

Mathematical Relationships

5. Resonant frequency, bandwidth, and "Q" of R-L-C circuits, given component values
6. Phase angle between voltage and current, given resistance and reactance
7. Power factor, given phase angle
8. Effective radiated power, given system gains and losses
9. Replacement of voltage source and resistive voltage divider with equivalent circuit consisting of a voltage source and one resistor (an application of thevenin's theorem, used to predict the current supplied by a voltage divider to a known load)

F. CIRCUIT COMPONENTS

Physical Appearance, Types, Characteristics, Applications, and Schematic Symbols for the Following:

1. Diodes; zener, tunnel, varactor, hot-carrier, junction, point contact, PIN
2. Transistors; npn, pnp, junction, unijunction, power, germanium, silicon
3. Silicon controlled rectifier, triac
4. Light emitting diode, neon lamp
5. Crystal lattice SSB filters

G. PRACTICAL CIRCUITS

1. Voltage regulator circuits; discrete and integrated
2. Amplifiers; class A, AB, B, C; characteristics of each type
3. Impedance matching networks; PI, L, PI-L
4. Filters; constant K, M-derived, band-stop, notch, modern-network-theory, PI-section, T-section, L-section (not necessary to memorize design equations; know description, characteristics, responses, and applications of these filters)
5. Oscillators; various types and their applications; stability

Transmitter and Receiver Circuits - Know Purpose of Each and How, Basically Each Functions:

6. Modulators; AM, FM, balanced
7. Transmitter final amplifiers
8. Detectors, mixer stages
9. RF and IF amplifier stages

Calculation of Voltages, Currents, and Power In Common Amateur Radio Oriented Circuits:

10. Common emitter class A transistor amplifier; bias network, signal gain, input and output impedances
11. Common collector class A transistor amplifier; bias network, signal gain, input and output impedances

Circuit Design; Selection of Circuit Component Values:

12. Voltage regulator with pass transistor and zener diode to produce given output voltage
13. Select coil and capacitor to resonate at given frequency

H. SIGNALS AND EMISSIONS

1. Emission types A4, A5, F4, F5
2. Modulation methods
3. Deviation ratio
4. Modulation index
5. Electromagnetic radiation
6. Wave polarization
7. Sine, square, sawtooth waveforms
8. Root mean square value
9. Peak envelope power relative to average
10. Signal to noise ratio

I. ANTENNAS AND FEEDLINES

1. Antenna gain, beamwidth
2. Trap antennas
3. Parasitic elements
4. Radiation resistance
5. Driven elements
6. Efficiency of antenna
7. Folded, multiple wire dipoles
8. Velocity factor
9. Electrical length of a feedline
10. Voltage and current nodes
11. Mobile antennas
12. Loading coil; base, center, top

STUDY TOPICS FOR THE AMATEUR EXTRA CLASS AMATEUR RADIO OPERATOR LICENSE EXAMINATION

A. RULES AND REGULATIONS

1. Frequency bands available to the U.S. amateur radio operator and limitations on their use including variations for regions 1 & 3 97.61; 97.95
2. Space amateur radio stations 97.3 (i)
3. Purity of emissions 97.73
4. Mobile operation aboard ships or aircraft 97.101
5. Races operation Part 97, Subpart F
6. Points of communications 97.89

B. OPERATING PROCEDURES

1. Use of amateur radio satellites
2. Amateur fast scan television

C. RADIO WAVE PROPAGATION

1. EME; "moonbounce"
2. Meteor burst
3. Trans-equatorial

D. AMATEUR RADIO PRACTICE

Use of Test Equipment:
1. Spectrum analyzer; interpret display; display of transmitter output spectrum, such as commonly found in new product review articles in amateur radio magazines
2. Logic probe; indication of high or low state, pulsing state

Electromagnetic Compatability:
3. Vehicle noise suppression; ignition noise, alternator whine, static
4. Direction finding techniques; methods for location of source of radio signals

E. ELECTRICAL PRINCIPLES

Concepts:
1. Photoconductive effect
2. Exponential charge/discharge

Mathematical Relationships; Calculations:
3. Time constant for R-C and R-L circuits (including circuits with more than one resistor, capacitor, or inductor)
4. Impedance diagrams; basic principles of Smith chart
5. Impedance of R-L-C networks at a specified frequency
6. Algebraic operations using complex numbers; real, imaginary, magnitude, angle

F. CIRCUIT COMPONENTS

Physical Appearance, Types, Characteristics, Applications, and Schematic Symbols for:
1. Field effect transistors; enhancement, depletion, MOS, CMOS, n-channel, p-channel
2. Operational amplifier and phase-locked loop integrated circuits
3. 7400 series TTL digital integrated circuits
4. 4000 series cmos digital integrated circuits
5. Vidicon; cathode ray tube

G. PRACTICAL CIRCUITS

1. Digital logic circuits; flip-flop, multivibrator, and/or/nand/nor/gates
3. ACtive audio filters using integrated operational amplifiers

High Performance Reciever Characteristics
4. Noise figure, sensitivity
5. Selectivity
6. Dynamic range

Calculation of Voltages, Currents, and Power In Common Amateur Radio Oriented Circuits:
7. Integrated operational amplifier; voltage gain, frequency response
8. F.E.T. common source amplifier; input impedance

Circuit Design; Selection of Circuit Component Values:
9. L-C preselector with fixed and variable capacitors to tune a given frequency range
10. Single stage amplifier to have desired frequency response by proper selection of bypass and coupling capacitors

H. SIGNALS AND EMISSIONS

1. Pulse modulation; position, width
2. Digital signals
3. Narrow band voice modulation
4. Information rate vs. bandwidth
5. Peak amplitude of signal
6. Peak-to-peak values of a signal

I. ANTENNAS AND FEEDLINES

1. Antennas for space radio communications; gain, beamwidth, tracking
2. Isotropic radiator; use as a standard of comparison
3. Phased vertical antennas; resultant patterns, spacing in wavelengths
4. Rhombic antennas; advantages, disadvantages
5. Matching antenna to feedline; delta, gamma, stub
6. Properties of 1/8, 1/4, 3/8 and 1/2 wavelength sections of feedlines; shorted, open

It's awfully "cutsey" to use a special phonetic alphabet over the air but it impedes communication, so **forget it**. If your call is SM6TG, the temptation to use "send me 6 tall girls" will be difficult, but fight the urge! Below is the International Telecommunication Union Phonetic Alphabet. Clip this out and keep it near your rig until you have it memorized and use it automatically.

ICAO Phonetic Alphabet

A - Alpha
B - Bravo
C - Charlie
D - Delta
E - Echo
F - Foxtrot
G - Golf
H - Hotel
I - India
J - Juliet
K - Kilo
L - Lima
M - Mike

N - November
O - Oscar
P - Papa
Q - Quebec
R - Romeo
S - Sierra
T - Tango
U - Uniform
V - Victor
W - Wiskey
X - X-ray
Y - Yankee
Z - Zulu

ILLEGIMENTI NON CORBORUNDUM

Our operation has received indications that the opposition (they reside in Washington) may try to shut us down. Therefore, we're soliciting your help to keep us alive. A "warchest" has been suggested for legal fund. Sounds like a good idea. Should you care to make a donation, please make your check payable to:

THE FINAL EXAM Legal Defense Fund
c/o Bash Educational Services
P.O. Box 2115
San Leandro, California 94577

Unlike some other pleas/requests for funds for legal services, this one's no ripoff. All contributors will receive a semi-annual accounting and no funds will be spent on anything except legal fees. Should it not be necessary to use the monies, they will be returned to the contributors with whatever interest has accumulated in the savings account.

Should any of you readers be an attorney with background/interest in Federal cases (such as ours could become), you are invited to contribute your special expertise. I and/or our counsel (Mike-K2GMV) will be glad to brief you upon receipt of your letterhead request. There's a 1st Amendment question here plus Title 5 problems. Should you have an interesting offensive or defensive scenario, please let us hear from you.

I wish I could personally thank each of you for your warm regards and illustrations of support. A simple "thank you" is hardly enough.

Below you will find a list of the various Q signals that you may need to use. A word of caution, though. These Q signals are intended for use during CW operations and are NOT designed for use during voice/A3/F3 transmissions. So, please don't be a turkey and go around saying, "My QTH is ..." or "Let's QSY" when you're on voice. It really will make you look dumb to the more knowledgeable hams and I **know** you don't want that.

A Q signal followed by a question mark is a question (logical, right?). If you leave off the question mark then you're making a statement.

QSA?	What is the name of your station?
QRB?	How far are you from my location?
QRD?	Where are you heading and where are you from?
QRG?	What is my exact frequency?
QRH?	Is my frequency varying?
QRI?	How does my tone sound to you? (T = 1 to 9)
QRK?	What is the readability of my signals? (R = 1 to 5)
QRL?	Are you busy?
*QRM?	Are you being interfered with?
*QRN?	Are you experiencing static noise?
QRO?	Should I increase power?
*QRP?	Should I decrease power?
QRQ?	Should I send faster?
*QRS?	Should I send slower?
*QRT?	Should I stop sending?
QRU?	Do you have any traffic/information for me?
QRV?	Are you ready?
QRW?	Should I tell ... that you are calling him/her on xxx KHz?
QRX?	When will you call me again?
*QRZ?	Who is calling me?
QSA?	What is my signal strength? (S = 1 to 9)
*QSB?	Are my signals fading?
QSD?	Is my keying faulty?
QSG?	Should I send .... messages at a time?
*QSK?	Are you able to work full break-in CW?
*QSL?	Do you confirm receipt of the information?
QSM?	Do you want me to repeat the last message?
QSN?	Did you hear me on .... KHz?
*QSO?	Can you communicate with .... direct?
QSW?	Will you transmit on .... KHz?
QSX?	Will you listen for .... on .... KHz?
*QSY?	Do you want me to change frequency?
QTA?	Do you want me to cancel message number ....?
QTB?	Do you agree with my word count?
QTC?	How many messages do you have to transmit?
*QTH?	What is your location?
QTR?	What is the correct time?

QTU? What hours will your station be on the air?
QTX? Will you keep your station open for further communications from me?
QUA? Do you have news of .... (callsign)?
QUC? What is the last message number you received from me?
QUF? Did you receive the distress call sent by .... (callsign)?
QUM? Has the distress traffic ended?

As you can readily discern, these are primarily intended for traffic (message) handling. You might want to put a copy of this near your rig if you're a traffic freak. The Q signals give the CW operator fewer things to transmit to get his message across and therefore are great for that purpose. Know what the ones with an asterik mean.

Practice Problems

Calculate the combined values of the capacitors below. Be careful to observe their relationship!

	C_1	C_2	relationship
a.	50 pF	30 pF	series
b.	50 pF	30 pF	parallel
c.	220 pF	10 pF	parallel
d.	750 pF	75 pF	series
e.	10 pF	16 pF	parallel
f.	75 mF	10 pF	series
g.	100 pF	70 mF	parallel
h.	30 mF	115 mF	series
i.	4 pF	150 mF	series
j.	8000 mF	15 pF	parallel

Home Remedies for TV Interference

HOME REMEDIES FOR RESOLVING RADIO TRANSMITTER INTERFERENCE

There are no set procedures for eliminating television interference—it is a matter of eliminating the most likely sources of interference a step at a time. The first step is to install an inexpensive high-pass filter on the back of your TV set. In making this installation, follow these procedures:

1. Determine the type of antenna wire that is connected to your TV set. There are two possibilities:

Coaxial Cable—a round lead-in wire which requires a filter "impedance" of 75 ohms. (See Figure 1a.)

Twin Lead Wire—a flat wire which requires a filter "impedance" of 300 ohms. (See Figure 1b.)

2. Purchase the filter which matches the type of antenna wire coming from your set. The "impedance" information mentioned above will be on the filter label. DO NOT use a combination of twin-lead and coaxial cable without proper matching transformers (often called baluns). Filters are available in most stores that sell or repair television sets. Figure 2 provides a small example of what high-pass filters look like.

3. Carefully read the instructions that are provided with the filter. You will be installing the filter on the back of your TV set, as near to the antenna terminal as possible. The antenna terminal and the filter terminal will look like either Figure 1a or 1b depending upon the type of wire you are using—coaxial or twin lead.

Installing A High-Pass Filter

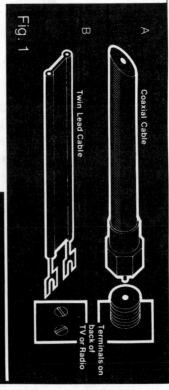

Fig. 1

A   Coaxial Cable

B   Twin Lead Cable

Terminals on back of TV or Radio

still install the filter at the antenna terminal. However, if the interference continues, contact the cable company repair service for assistance. DO NOT attempt to modify the cable system yourself.

5. The following information on installing the filter should answer any additional questions you may have.

a. Disconnect the antenna wire (twin-lead or coaxial) from the television set antenna terminals.

b. Connect the wire from the antenna to the input terminals of the filter.

c. For twin-lead wire, connect a very short (1" to 2") "jumper" wire from the antenna input terminals of the set to the filter (see Figure 3). For coaxial cable, it will be necessary to obtain a jumper cable that has the proper connectors already installed. (This can be purchased at the time you buy the coaxial filter.)

d. Be sure that in the case of **TWIN-LEAD WIRE**, the actual wires are making

4. If you are on a cable system, you may

Fig. 2

Montage of Filters

90

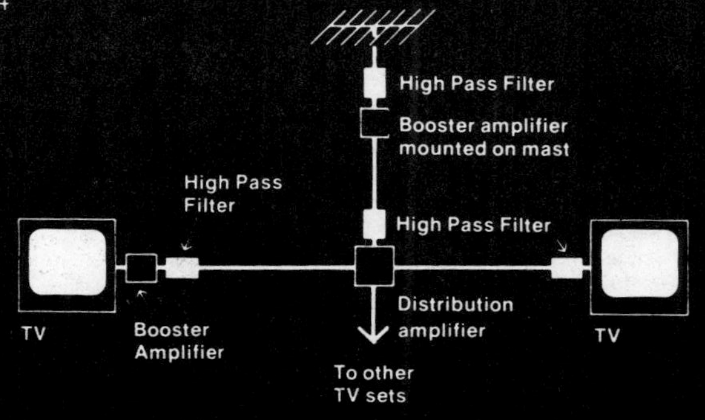

contact with the terminals. For **COAXIAL CABLE,** be sure the connector plugs are properly installed on the coaxial cable.

e. If you have an amplifier in your antenna system, you should have a filter installed ahead of the amplifier and another filter ahead of the TV receiver input terminals (see Figure 4). If the amplifier is located close to the receiver, then install the filter before the amplifier only.

Note: BOOSTER amplifiers usually are located near the back of the TV set; MAST MOUNTED (Outdoor) amplifiers are usually located on the antenna; and DISTRIBUTION amplifiers are usually located somewhere in the distribution system. If a distribution amplifier is in your antenna system, then be sure to trace the entire length of the antenna system, because amplifiers are usually in out-of-the-way places (for example—clothes closets, basements, etc.)

f. The connecting wires between the filter and amplifier, and between the amplifier and antenna terminal, should be as short as possible.

g. The instructions provided with the filter you bought may call for a ground connection. The wire should be as short as possible and connected between the high-pass filter ground terminal and a metallic cold water pipe or a ground rod. Use bell wire for this connection (see Figure 3). Bell wire can be obtained from most variety stores.

h. If installation of the filter at the TV antenna terminals does not entirely eliminate the interference, you should then contact your service representative to install a high-pass filter inside the TV set at the tuner

Fig. 3

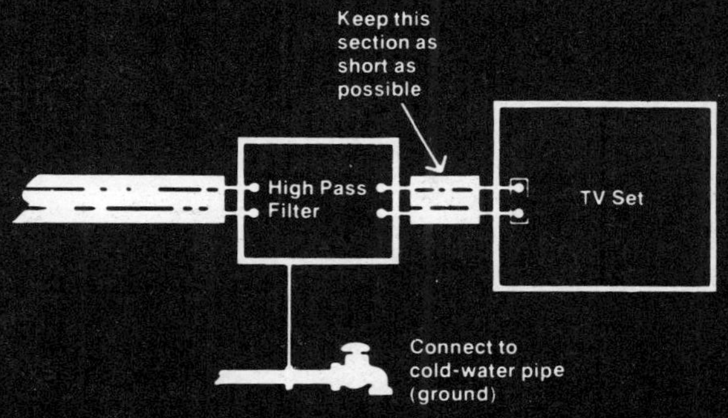

Keep this section as short as possible

TV Set

High Pass Filter

Connect to cold-water pipe (ground)

Fig. 4

High Pass Filter

Booster amplifier mounted on mast

High Pass Filter

Distribution amplifier

To other TV sets

High Pass Filter

Booster Amplifier

TV

TV

input terminals. INTERNAL modifications to your set should be done ONLY by a service representative. Information to assist your service representative is contained in the Technical Information for Service Representatives section.

Home Remedies for Resolving Electrical Interference

Electrical interference is caused by two sources:

1. Vehicle ignition systems.
2. Electrical devices.

The first step in attempting to resolve electrical interference problems is to locate the source of interference.

Interference from Vehicle Ignition System

1. Ignition interference sounds like a "popping" noise in the sound system of your TV that rises in intensity; the "pops" occur closer and closer ,ogether as the speed of the engine speeds up. This can be caused by any vehicle ignition system, such as gasoline operated lawn mowers, snowmobiles, automobiles, etc.

2. If the interference is to television receivers, you may hear the same popping noise in the sound and also see "dancing dots" in the picture of the set. You may only see the interference, and not hear the "popping" noise in the sound.

3. If your own vehicle is causing interference, you may wish to install a commercially manufactured kit in your vehicle to reduce the ignition noise. Other remedial measures include relocating your antenna, raising the antenna, and using shielded lead-in antenna wire.

Interference from Electrical Devices

1. Any one or more of the following electrical devices may be causing the interference you are experiencing on your television set or AM/FM radio:

Electric razor, Vacuum cleaner, Fan, Drill, Electric blankets, Bake ovens, Fluorescent lights, Arc lights, Light dimmer controls, Relays, Static from machinery, Lightning arrestors, Adding machine, Cash register, Circuit breakers, Ultra-violet lamps, Germicidal lamps, Defective wiring, Loose fuse, Arc welder, Switch contacts (such as on dishwashers and other home appliances), Refrigerator, Water pump, Sewing machine, Light blinkers (including Christmas tree light blinker), Electric heating pads, Aquarium warmers, Neon signs, Door bell circuits/ transformers, Toys (such as electric trains), Sign flashers, Antifriction bearings, Printing press static eliminators, Calculator, Insulation, Incandescent lamp (new or old), Sun lamps, Electrical pole (ground wire cut or poor contact), Loose electrical connection, Electric fence unit, Furnace controls, Power company transformers, Smoke precipitators.

2. In attempting to locate the specific device causing the interference, consider the following suggestions:

a. If you have a portable radio that is affected by the interference, use the radio as a detection device to assist in locating the source of interference. With the portable radio, move from room to room and determine in which room the interference appears to be the loudest. Then look for one of the devices listed above and unplug it to see if the interference disappears. If several devices listed above are in the room, unplug them, one at a time, until the interference disappears.

b. If a portable radio is not affected, you can go to the main fuse or circuit breaker box in your home, remove one fuse at a time, or shut off one breaker at a time, and see if the interference goes away.

c. If it does not go away when the first fuse or circuit breaker is off, replace the fuse or turn the circuit breaker back on and continue on until the interference does disappear. When the circuit that supplies the power to the TV or radio is turned off, it will be necessary to plug that device into some other circuit to determine if the interference is being generated by a device in the same room as your TV or radio.

d. When the interference disappears with a fuse removed or circuit breaker off, you should go to the room supplied by that circuit and look for any of the devices listed above. If any of the listed devices are found in the room, replace the fuse or turn the circuit breaker back on. Then unplug the device suspected of causing the interference. If several devices are in the room, unplug them, one at a time.

3. If you are unable to locate within your own home the device that is causing the problem, the interference may be coming from a device located in your neighbor's home. With the cooperation of your neighbor, follow the same procedures described above.

4. If your investigation leads you to suspect that a power line or power company equipment is the source of interference, you should contact the power company to assist you in resolving the problem.

5. Short duration interference, such as that from electric drills and saws, may be very costly to attempt to eliminate; you may just want to "live with it."

6. To *resolve* electrical interference, modifications must be made to the interfering device. This should only be done by a qualified service representative. Information for your service representative is contained in the Technical Information for Service Representatives section.

Home Remedies for Resolving FM Interference

The installation of an inexpensive FM band rejection filter is the first step to take in resolving FM interference. In making this installation, follow these procedures:

1. Determine the type of antenna wire you have connected to your TV set. There are two possibilities:

Coaxial Cable—a round lead-in wire which requires a filter "impedance" of 75 ohms (see Figure 1a).

Twin Lead Wire—a flat wire which requires a filter "impedance" of 300 ohms (see Figure 1b).

2. Purchase the appropriate filter, according to the type of antenna wire you have. The "impedance" information mentioned above will be on the filter label. DO NOT use a combination of twin-lead and coaxial cable without proper matching transformers (often called baluns). Filters are available in most stores that sell or repair television sets.

3. Carefully read the instructions that are provided with the filter. You will be installing the filter on the back of your TV set, as near to the antenna terminal as possible. The antenna terminal and the filter terminal will look like either Figure 1a or 1b depending upon the type of wire you are using—coaxial cable or twin-lead wire.

4. If you are on a cable system, you may still install the same FM band rejection filter at the antenna terminal. However, if the interference continues, contact the cable company repair service for assistance. DO NOT attempt to modify the cable system yourself.

5. The following information on installing the filter should answer any additional questions you may have.

a. Disconnect the antenna wire (twin-lead or coaxial) from the television set antenna terminals.

b. Connect the wire from the antenna to the input terminals of the filter.

c. For twin-lead wire, connect a very short (1" to 2") "jumper" wire from the antenna input terminals of the set to the filter (see Figure 3). For coaxial cable, it will be necessary to obtain a jumper cable that has the proper connectors already installed.

d. Be sure that in the case of TWIN LEAD WIRE, the actual wires are making contact with the terminals. For COAXIAL CABLE, be sure the connector plugs are properly installed on the coaxial cable.

e. If you have an amplifier in your antenna system, you should have a filter installed before the amplifier and another filter ahead of the TV receiver input terminals (see Figure 4). If the amplifier is located close to the receiver, then install the filter before the amplifier only.

Note: BOOSTER amplifiers usually are located near the back of the TV set; MAST MOUNTED (outdoor) amplifiers are usually located on the antenna; and DISTRIBUTION amplifiers are usually located somewhere in the distribution system. If a distribution amplifier is in your antenna system, then be sure to trace the entire length of the antenna system, because amplifiers are usually in out-of-the-way places (for example—clothes closets, basements, etc.)

f. The connecting wires between the filter and amplifier, and between the amplifier and antenna terminal, should be as short as possible.

g. The instructions provided with the filter you bought may call for a ground connection. The wire should be as short as possible and connected between the FM band rejection filter ground terminal and a metallic cold water pipe or a ground rod. Use bell wire for this connection (see Figure 3). Bell wire can be obtained from most variety stores.

h. If the filter does not entirely eliminate the interference, you should call your service representative. The Technical Information for Service Representatives Section is provided to assist the service representative.

Audio Interference

Identification of Audio Interference

Interference to audio devices, such as tape recorders, record players, electronic organs, telephones, hi-fi amplifiers, etc., is caused when the equipment responds to the transmission of a nearby radio transmitter.

Audio interference (often called audio rectification) may also affect the sound (audio) portion of your TV and AM/FM radio.

When this type of interference is occurring, you will hear the voice transmissions of the radio transmitter and/or the volume level of the audio device you are using may decrease.

If you have determined that this is the type of interference you are receiving, refer to the following Home Remedies section for suggested methods for eliminating audio interference.

Home Remedies for Resolving Audio Interference

Audio interference is a condition that usually requires internal modification of your equipment. For safety reasons, it is recommended that any modifications be made by a qualified service representative.

Due to the complexity of resolving interference to an electronic organ, again, servicing should be done only by an experienced service representative. More detailed information should be obtained from the equipment manufacturer.

For telephone interference, contact your local telephone company. They can install a 1542A or similar inductor in the telephone instrument to resolve the problem. The information provided in this bulletin applies primarily to privately-owned equipment and should not be applied to equipment owned by the telephone company. Bell System personnel can obtain additional data in Section 500-150-100 of the "Bell System Practices—Plant Series" manual.

For all other audio devices, you may wish to take the following steps before calling your service representative.

1. Replace UNSHIELDED wire between the amplifier and speakers with SHIELDED wire.

2. Ground the affected equipment to a metallic cold water pipe or ground rod. A ground connection can be made with a short piece of "bell wire" which can be obtained at most variety stores. DO NOT ground "AC-DC" type devices. Normally devices which may safely be grounded will provide a grounding terminal. If no terminal is provided, then you should consult a qualified service representative for advice.

3. If the interference is not eliminated after taking these steps you must call a qualified service representative. The Technical Information for Service Representatives section is provided to assist your service representative in resolving the problem. You may also wish to discuss the matter with the operator of the radio transmitter, sharing the information in the Radio Operator Guidelines section of this bulletin.

94

Technical Information

Technical Information for Service Representatives

Resolving Radio Transmitter Interference

There are no set procedures for eliminating television interference—it is a matter of eliminating the most likely sources of interference a step at a time. You may be required to take several steps before the interference problem is resolved. Once you have installed the filter called for, or made the adjustment that you were instructed to do, leave the modifications in place and proceed to the next step.

To begin, check to see if a high-pass filter has been installed on the TV set at the antenna terminals. If not, read the Home Remedy information beginning on page 5. If the interference is still present after the installation of a high-pass filter proceed with the following steps.

Check Radio Transmitter

1. Contact the operator of the radio transmitter identified as the source and, with his/her cooperation, determine if the transmitter is operating properly. You may also wish to share the Radio Operator Guidelines section of this bulletin with the operator. Areas of concern should be:

a. Is the transmitter properly grounded? (This means a good radio frequency (**RF**) ground. A single piece of wire to a ground rod may be an open circuit to **RF**.)

b. Are harmonics and/or spurious emissions present?

c. Is the transmitter cabinet radiating energy?

2. If the transmitter is not grounded, connect the chassis to a good earth ground with large diameter wire or copper strap. This should assist in eliminating radiation of energy from the cabinet.

3. Next, install a low-pass filter on the transmitter antenna circuit to see if any difference occurs in the interference pattern. If a change occurs, the interference is probably caused by harmonics and/or spurious emissions from the transmitter. If no change occurs in the interference pattern, it is probably being generated at some point in the TV reception system.

Check TV Reception System

1. Conduct a visual inspection of the TV antenna, lead-in wire, and lightning arrestors. This may reveal a source of trouble. Corroded connections or deteriorated lead-in wire could be at fault and should be repaired.

2. Assuming no faulty conditions are found, or if found, they are corrected, and the interference is still present, look for an amplifier in the line. Amplifiers are highly susceptible to radio frequency (**RF**) energy.

Note: BOOSTER amplifiers usually are located near the back of the TV set; MAST MOUNTED (outdoor) amplifiers are usually located on the antenna; and DISTRIBUTION amplifiers are usually located somewhere in the distribution system. If a distribution amplifier is in the antenna system, then be sure to trace the entire length of the antenna system, because amplifiers are usually in out-of-the-way places (for example—clothes closets, basements, etc.).

3. If an amplifier is in the system, remove it from the circuit. If you find that this eliminates the interference, reconnect the amplifier, but protect the amplifier by a) grounding, b) enclosing it in a metallic rf-proof housing and grounding the housing, or c) installing a high-pass filter at the input to the amplifier. If one filter improves the condition, but does not entirely eliminate the interference, install two filters in series.

4. If no amplifier is utilized, or the interference still persists after following one or all of the above steps, check the TV receiver system.

Check TV Receiver System

1. An AC power line **RF** filter should be installed to determined if the **RF** from the transmitter is entering the TV via the power cord. (A line filter may be either purchased or one may be constructed by following the schematic in Figure 5.)

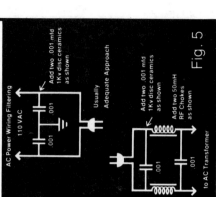

AC Power Wiring Filtering

110 VAC

Add two .001 mfd 1Kv disc ceramics as shown

Usually Adequate Approach

to AC Transformer

Add two .001 mfd 1Kv disc ceramics as shown

Add two 50mH RF Chokes as shown

Fig. 5

95

2. If no change is found with the power line filter installed, and the antenna disconnected, then the set itself is responding to the **RF** energy.

3. The most likely internal circuit in the set to be affected by a radio transmitter is the tuner. Disconnect the antenna input lead inside the set directly at the tuner. If the interference is eliminated, then install a high-pass filter at the tuner.

4. If the interference is still present after installing the filter at the tuner, it will be necessary to refer to service data for the set and check each stage of the set for undesired response.

CB Interference to TV Channel 2

1. Second harmonic interference from a CB transmitter to Channel 2 television may exist even though the transmitter meets FCC specifications for harmonic radiation. In such cases, a tuned filter across the antenna terminals of the television should help. The filter may be an inductor and capacitor in series as in Figure 6. The filter should be tuned for minimum interference.

2. A second method is to put an open circuit, quarter-wave, tuned stub across the antenna terminals. The stub should be made of the same type of wire as the antenna input terminals of the television. The initial stub length should be 37" for RG-59/U coax; and 48" for 300 ohm twin lead.

3. After connecting the stub, cut the unterminated end of the stub off in 1/8" to 1/4" sections until the interference is eliminated. Refer to Figure 7. For harmonics falling on other TV channels, such as channel 5, 6, or

9. the length of the stub may be appropriately shortened according to the following formula.

$$\text{Length in inches} = \frac{2952V}{f}$$

where **V** = Velocity factor of line
and **f** = frequency in megahertz

Amateur Interference to TV Channel 2

1. One additional type of interference from a nearby transmitter is unique to the amateur 6 meter band—50 - 54 MHz. Since 6 meters is immediately adjacent to Channel 2 television (54 - 60 MHz), interference to Channel 2 may occur.

2. In most cases, installation of an open circuit, quarterwave, tuned stub at the antenna terminals of the television set should be effective. It should be connected as shown in Figure 7.

3. If RG-59/U is used as the TV lead-in wire, the initial length of the stub should be 42". If 300 ohm twin lead is used, the initial length should be 53".

4. After the stub is attached to the television, begin cutting off the unterminated end of the stub 1/8" to 1/4" at a time until the interference is eliminated. If the interference is reduced, but not eliminated by this method, add a second stub directly to the input terminals of the tuner. The theoretical final length of the stub should be:

$$\text{Length in inches} = \frac{2952V}{f}$$

Where **V** = Velocity factor of line
and **f** = frequency in megahertz

5. If the interference continues, share the information in the Radio Operator Guidelines section with the operator of the radio transmitter.

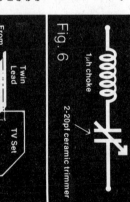

Fig. 6

1 µh choke

2 - 20pf ceramic trimmer

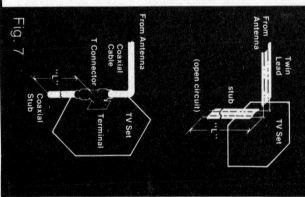

From Antenna

Twin Lead

stub

(open circuit)

"L"

TV Set

Fig. 7

From Antenna

Coaxial Cable

T Connector

Terminal

"L"

Coaxial Stub

TV Set

96

Resolving Electrical Interference

1. Please read through the procedures outlined in the Home Remedies section, beginning on page 7, before proceeding. If the steps in the previous section have been taken, you should now know the source of the interference.

2. Before proceeding with the following steps to modify the device located as the source of interference, you should check the local electrical codes to determine if the device may be modified, and whether a licensed electrician must modify the device.

Caution: All bypassing of devices with capacitors should be done with extreme care to insure that the capacitors do not short out the AC line. Dangerous voltages exist which can cause electrocution if mishandled. Also, avoid power wiring which can cause the full AC line voltage to appear on the case of the device.

3. Since interference from an electric drill or saw may be of short duration, we suggest no modifications be made to the device. Mainly because it may be very difficult and time-consuming to modify the device. If, however, interference is of long duration, and you wish to take on this task, proceed as follows:

a. Interference from a drill or saw is actually caused by arcing between the brushes and commutator. The interference then is transmitted through the power cord. Bypassing each side of the line to ground with a capacitor, and each side to the other may be helpful. Also bypass the switch. Figure 8 shows the schematic involved. The bypassing should be internal to the device in question.

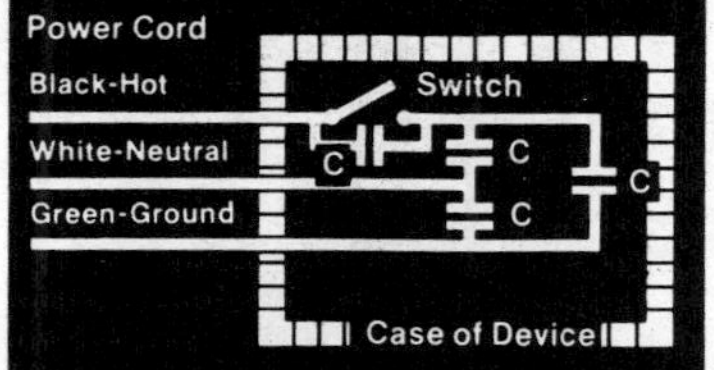

Power Cord
Black-Hot
White-Neutral
Green-Ground
Switch
Case of Device

Fig. 8

C =.001 mfd., disc ceramic

.001 mfd... disc ceramic

Fig. 9

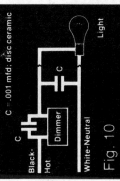

C = .001 mfd: disc ceramic

Black-Hot
Dimmer
White-Neutral
Light

Fig. 10

4. Electric blankets, fish tank heaters, and other thermostatically controlled appliances, with worn and pitted contacts, cause interference because of contact arcing of the breaker points. This can be eliminated by bypassing the contacts with a .001 mfd capacitor or replacing the worn or pitted contacts. (See Figure 9.)

5. Defective devices such as doorbell transformers should be replaced.

6. Dimmer switches that utilize an SCR or triac can produce tremendous interference and it is very difficult to eliminate. This is due to the approximate square wave output that is produced by the switching at the SCR or triac. However, bypassing in a manner shown in Figure 10 may be helpful.

7. Since resolving electrical interference has to proceed on a case-by-case basis, you should always consider adequately bypassing any component of the circuit that arcs or distorts the AC sine wave with ceramic condensers.

Resolving FM Interference

There are no set procedures for eliminating FM interference—it is a matter of eliminating the most likely sources of interference a step at a time. You may be required to take several steps before the interference problem is resolved. Once you have installed the filter called for, or made the adjustment that you were instructed to do, leave the modifications in place and proceed to the next step.

1. To begin, check to see if an FM band rejection filter has been installed on the TV set at the antenna terminals. If not, read the Home Remedies section of this bulletin, beginning on page 8.

2. If the installation of an FM band rejection filter is not effective, then a tuned stub

trap should be constructed (see example in Figure 11). The trap should be placed on and parallel to the lead-in and tuned for minimum interference. Then slide the trap along the line to further reduce interference. Finally, tape the trap to the lead-in in the most effective position.

3. Another type of stub, called an open circuit quarter-wave type, can be made from the same type of wire as the antenna lead-in wire (see Figure 12). The initial length of the stub should be 24" for RG-59/U coaxial cable or 29" for 300 ohm twin-lead wire. For other cables, the initial length can be determined by the general formula:

Length in inches = (35) (Velocity factor of line)

Note: If "F" type tee connectors are not available, you may use BNC type connectors.

4. If connecting the stub to the antenna terminals is not completely effective, connect a second stub of the same length directly to the input terminals of the tuner, inside the television set. This should eliminate the interference.

Resolving Audio Interference

1. Audio interference is defined as reception of radio frequency (**RF**) energy by an audio amplifier. The **RF** energy is then rectified, or more properly "detected", by an electron tube, transistor, diode, poor solder joint or ground, or integrated circuit. The detected signal is then treated identically as a normal audio signal appearing at the amplifier input terminals. The effects of audio interference vary with the type of modulation employed by the transmitter. The following chart shows expected effects:

AM—The voice or music will be heard as any normal audio signal applied to the amplifier. The voice or music may be extremely loud and slightly distorted.

SSB—Single Sideband—The voice will sound practically unintelligible and garbled.

FM—Usually no sound will be heard; however, a decrease in the volume of the amplifier will be noted when the radio transmitter is on. Clicks may be heard when a two-way radio transmitter is keyed and unkeyed. A "frying" noise (such as bacon sizzling) may also be heard.

TV—Audio rectification of a TV signal will sound like a buzz. The buzz will change its sound as the television picture changes.

2. In attempting to isolate where in the audio chain the rectification is taking place, check to determine if the volume control has any effect on the interference. If the volume of the interfering signal changes with a change in the volume control, then the rectification is occurring BEFORE the volume control. If the volume control has minimal or no effect, the rectification is occurring AFTER the volume control. You should next proceed to the appropriate set of solutions. If the solutions described below do not resolve the audio interference problem, contact the manu-

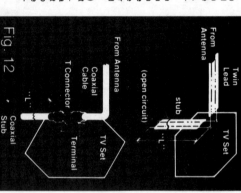

Fig. 11

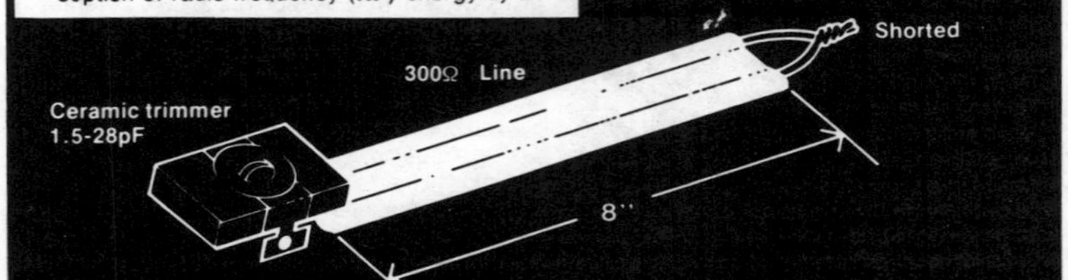

Ceramic trimmer
1.5-28pF

300Ω Line

8"

Shorted

Fig. 12

From Antenna

Twin Lead

(open circuit)

stub

TV Set

From Antenna

Coaxial Cable

T Connector

Terminal

"L"

TV Set

"L" Coaxial Stub

facturer of the audio device for further assistance.

Rectification Before the Volume Control

1. A multiple input audio amplifier may be susceptible to audio interference on only one or some of the available inputs. Generally, low-level, high-impedance inputs, such as those in turn-tables, cartridges, tape heads, or microphones, are the most susceptible. If, for example, the only input affected is from a turn-table, then disconnect the turn-table cartridge from the amplifier at the input terminals of the amplifier.

2. If the interference is eliminated, then the cartridge, or wire between the cartridge and amplifier, is sensing the **RF**. Proper grounding, connections, shielding, and **RF** bypassing are the keys to solving audio rectification. Often, a "process of elimination" approach must be used.

Grounding

1. All grounding should be to a good earth ground such as a metallic cold water pipe or 8' ground rod. Ground leads should be as short as possible. Remember, a DC ground may appear as an open circuit to **RF** energy. Ground leads should be of as large a diameter wire as practicable. Finally, grounding of the chassis, shields of speaker leads, and other external connections should be made to a common point to avoid ground loops. (Ground loops are circuits that form a DC ground, but contain RF circulating currents.) Figure 15 shows the correct and incorrect methods of grounding components.

Caution: Some equipment chassis are at line voltage potential and cannot be connected directly to ground. In these circumstances, a ceramic capacitor of 0.001 mfd at 1Kv should be placed in the ground lead. This capacitor appears as a short to **RF**, but an open circuit to AC.

Shielding

1. All speaker leads from audio equipment should be made of two conductor shielded wires. The shield should be grounded only at the amplifier end, and should not be used as an audio conductor. The two internal wires should be connected to the speaker.

Power Line Filter

1. **RF** may be entering the audio device through the AC power line. Several power line filters are commercially available. If necessary, a power line filter like the one shown in Figure 5 may be constructed, placing the filter as close as possible to the point where the AC cord enters the amplifier.

Poor Electrical Connections

1. Occasionally, poor solder connections or old electrolytic capacitors may be the cause of the audio rectification problem. If tests to this point have failed, try resoldering all connections in the amplifier and replacing electrolytic capacitors. Before actually replacing the electrolytic capacitor, try paralleling the capacitor with another one of like value. This should reveal the presence of a bad capacitor.

Rectification After the Volume Control

1. When the volume control is in its minimum position, and the interference is still heard, then an **RF** filter is required in the audio amplifier. It is extremely important that

Wrong

Tuner
Tape Recorder
Record Player
Amplifier

this "loop" may act like an antenna at some frequency

Right

Tuner
Tape Recorder
Record Player
Amplifier
Earth Ground

Fig. 13

99

the filter does not affect the audio response of the amplifier.

Tube Type Equipment

1. Interference in tube type equipment can be avoided by connecting an RF choke (ranging in value from 2 millihenry to 5 millihenry) in the upper end of the cathode circuit as shown in Figure 14.

2. The choke coil must NOT be bypassed by a capacitor because the DC resistance of such coil is generally quite low and the bias voltage is not greatly affected. However, if the DC resistance does affect the bias voltage, the value of the bias resistor may be decreased to compensate for the DC resistance of the choke.

3. A grid-stopping or "swamping" resistor can also be employed. A resistor, ranging in value from 1 k to 75 k ohms, can be connected in series with the grid as shown in Figure 15.

4. Capacitors, **RF** chokes and resistors can be used in combinations to make filters to eliminate the interference. For circuits such as those shown in Figure 16, use a choke of 2 to 6 microhenries and a capacitor of about 10 picofards. A combination RF filter is shown in Figure 17 with the recommended values.

Transistor Equipment

1. Interference in transistor equipment can usually be eliminated with the use of a shunt capacitor as shown in Figure 18. A resistor/capacitor combination can be used as shown in Figure 19. It is important that the filter network does not affect the biasing of the transistor or the frequency response of the amplifier.

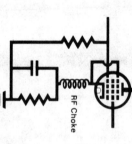

Fig. 14

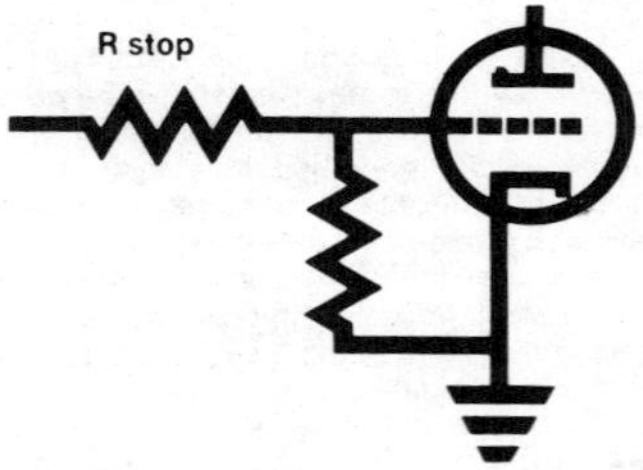

RF Choke

Fig. 15

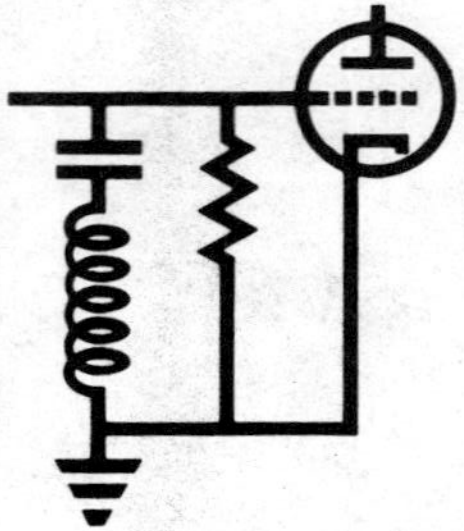

R stop

A combination RC filter is shown in Figure 17 with the recommended values.

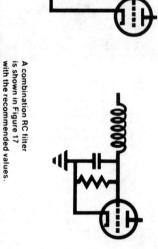

Fig. 16

2. The values of the capacitors used are not critical, but there are some pitfalls to look out for in using capacitors. For example, ceramic caps are best, whereas paper caps do not work at radio frequencies.

3. Leads should be kept as short as possible. Grounds should be made directly to the emitter and not to the chassis or other grounds, since they may have more **RF** than the signal lead. If the signal increases, then a ground loop has been created, and the inductor method should be tried.

4. In areas of high **RF** energy, the inductor approach is more effective than the shunt capacitor. An **RF** choke can be used in series with the input and output leads of the amplifier stage since the **RF** can enter a stage through either. This method and the values are shown in Figure 20.

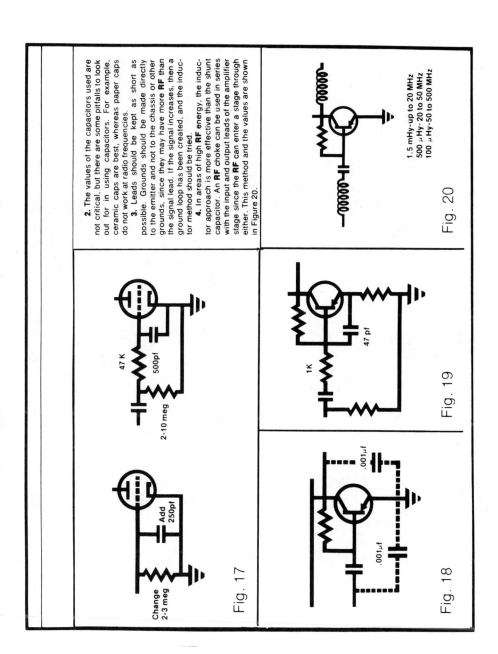

1.5 mHy-up to 20 MHz
500 μHy- 20 to 50 MHz
100 μHy-50 to 500 MHz

Fig. 20

Fig. 19

Fig. 18

Change 2-3 meg
Add 250pf
47 K
500pf
2-10 meg

Fig. 17

1K
47 pf

.001μf
.001μf

Electronic Organs

1. Organ circuits can be isolated by the use of the Swell Pedal, band box volume, or tabs (draw bars). By adjusting each one of these different controls, the effect on the interference can be noted. If the volume of the interference changes, the RF is being detected by the amplifier at a point before that particular control. If the volume of the interference does not change, then the interference is being detected after that control.

2. Using this method, the point at which the **RF** is entering the organ can be determined, and the appropriate filter, as described above, can be inserted into the circuit.

Telephones

1. Telephone **RF** interference can be eliminated by the use of a 1542A or similar inductor. This inductor must be installed inside the phone and not at the baseboard. To install the inductor inside the phone, the corners of the plastic container will have to be removed. If the phone is too small for the inductor, such as the "Princess" telephone, then a pair of 2.5 MH chokes (75 ma or higher) must be installed inside the phone, one on each side of the line and as close to the 211A equalizing network as possible.

Note: The information provided here applies primarily to privately owned equipment and should not be applied to equipment owned by the telephone company. Telephone company owned equipment should be modified only by telephone company personnel. Bell System personnel can obtain additional data in Section 500-150-100 of the "Bell System Practices—Plant Series" manual.

References

1. The *Audio Cyclopedia* by Howard M. Tremline, Howard W. Sams and Co., Inc.

2. *Radio Handbook* by William I. Orr, Editors and Engineers, Ltd.

3. *The Radio Amateur's Handbook* by American Radio Relay League.

4. *Thomas Tech-Flash*, Thomas Organ Co., Sepulveda, California.

5. "Filtering RF Interference in Audio Equipment", by R. S. MacCollister from Journal of the Audio Engineering Society, April 1968, Pages 210, 212, 214.

6. *Stopping Telephone Interference* by Irvin M. Hoff, QST, March 1968, Pages 46-47.

Radio Transmitter Operator Guidelines

Resolution of Interference for Radio Transmitter Operators

Although some interference problems can be attributed to television receivers, such problems can also be traced to CB radio transmitters. Therefore, upon receipt of an interference complaint from your neighbor(s), you should take all steps possible to insure that your radio transmitter is not causing the interference. Voluntary installation of a low-pass filter, or other steps as outlined below, may eliminate the interference, and may prevent you from receiving an order from the Commission to implement these measures. You are not, however, required to service or add filtering to the complainant's television, and should not take any such action without the full cooperation of your neighbors.

You are cautioned that the use of an amateur transceiver on the Citizens Band is illegal. Further, the use of external **RF** power amplifiers with CB transceivers is illegal. Both actions may subject you to Commission actions or criminal penalties.

Generally, transmitter equipment that is commercially manufactured and type-accepted by the Commission has precautions built into the set to reduce harmonic radiation. Harmonics are radiations that are multiples of the operating frequency. However, you should follow the steps outlined below to insure that your radio equipment is operating properly.

1. If television interference is occurring, note which channels are affected.

a. Lower harmonics of CB generally affect TV Channels 2, 5, 6, and 9. Therefore, if one or more of these channels are affected,

your transmitter is probably radiating harmonics.

b. If all TV channels are affected, the problem is more likely to be in the TV receiver.

2. If the interference is caused by harmonics, a spectrum analyzer, a calibrated field intensity meter, or frequency selective voltmeter, can be used to accurately measure harmonic and spurious radiations from your transmitter. If any lead-in devices, such as standing wave ratio (SWR) meters are used, measurements should be made with the in-line device both installed and removed. This may help identify the interference and lead you to the source. These are complex measurements and should normally be made only by experienced technicians.

3. If it appears that your transmitter is at fault, you should first make sure the chassis of the set is secured to the metal case of the radio by tightening the screws holding the chassis and case together. Then assure that the case of the transmitter is grounded to a good earth ground (metallic cold water pipe or 8 foot ground rod). Solid conductor wire of at least #10 gauge or copper ribbon should be used as a ground lead. The lead should be as short as possible.

4. By installing one or more low-pass filters in the transmitter antenna lead, you will reduce the chances of unnecessary harmonic radiation. A low-pass filter allows frequencies up to 30 or 50 megahertz (MHz), depending on brand, to pass through unattenuated to the antenna while effectively shorting out harmonic radiation. To make this test, connect the equipment as in Figure 21 and take a power reading. If only an SWR Bridge is available, calibrate it in the forward direction to the

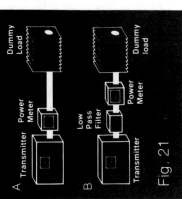

Fig. 21

calibrate line in the meter. Then insert the low-pass filter and make another power measurement. DO NOT retune the transmitter.

5. If you notice a decrease in output power or on a power meter, operating to a properly matched load, with the low-pass filter installed, this is an indication that harmonic content may be present. Even though the meter reading may be lower with the filter installed, it does not mean that the transmitter absolutely has harmonic radiation. Slight de-tuning of the transmitter by the filter may cause a lower indication.

6. At amateur power levels, corroded metal connections in the area of the transmitting antenna may act like diodes and generate harmonics which may radiate. This type of problem can be found by vibrating suspected offenders such as galvanized downspouts, metal fences, clothes lines, etc., while viewing the affected television set. Sudden changes in the interference pattern which correspond to the vibration should be noted. This test requires an observer at the TV receiver, someone to "shake" suspicious metal objects in the area, and another person to key (but NOT modulate) the transmitter involved.

7. Finally, some transmitters may actually be radiating harmonic and spurious energy from their cabinet or through the power lines. Try operating the transmitter into a shielded dummy load. If the interference is still present, then cabinet or power line radiation is indicated. A power line filter should be installed. Several types are commercially available. For low power transmitters, the filter in Figure 5 may be used.

8. Continued interference with the power line filter installed points toward cabinet radiation. An earth ground should eliminate cabinet radiation.

9. Local Television Interference (TVI) Committees dedicated to resolving CB-TVI problems are now being established. For assistance in locating a TVI Committee in your area, contact: International CB Radio Operator's Association (CBA), P.O. Box 1020, Roanoke, Va., 24005.

Resolution of Interference for Amateur Transmitter Operators

1. If you have a linear amplifier on your amateur transmitting equipment, use two low-pass filters. One filter should be installed between the actual transmitter (exciter) and the input to the linear amplifier. (This prevents harmonics generated in the exciter from reaching the linear amplifier.) The second filter should be installed at the output of the linear amplifier to reduce harmonic and spurious content.

2. One unique interference problem to TV Channel 2 is from an amateur transmitter operating on the 6 meter band. This is due to the close proximity of the frequencies involved. You may wish to follow the procedures outlined in the Technical Information for Service Representatives section, page 11, to eliminate this type interference. You are not, however, required to service or add filtering to the complainant's television, and should not take any such action without the full cooperation of your neighbor.

3. Local Television Interference (TVI) Committees are available to assist you in resolving interference problems. Contact the nearest FCC district office (see addresses beginning on page 28) or the American Radio Relay League, Newington, Connecticut, for assistance in locating a TVI committee in your area.

Radio Transmitter Operator Guidelines for Resolving Audio Interference

Although audio interference (often called audio rectification) is usually resolved by modification of the affected device, you as a radio operator can take certain steps to reduce the possibility of audio frequency (RF) currents in grounds and metal objects in the area.

1. Your radio transmitting equipment should be effectively grounded to a metallic cold water pipe or a ground rod driven into the ground at least 8 feet. The ground lead must be at least #10 wire or copper ribbon. The greater the surface area of the ground lead, the more effective it will be. Also, the ground lead should be as short as possible.

2. You are reminded that you are licensed to use only the amount of power necessary to establish communications. Operating with excessive power is likely to cause audio interference problems.

3. If you need assistance in performing the above modifications to your equipment, you can contact the dealer or manufacturer representatives. Also, an FCC-licensed service representative may be able to assist you.

HOURS OF OPERATION

You may telephone us at 415-352-5420 from 1800 - 0100 Zulu time during the months of April through October or from 1900 - 0200 Zulu during the months of November through March. If you haven't figured out Zulu time/GMT/UCT yet (why?), then please refer to the chart below that describes the time conversions. Use Daylight Savings Time (E.D.S.T., C.D.S.T., etc) from April through October and use the "regular" time columns for November through March.

During other times there will be a recording on the telephone where you may leave a message. Because of the expense involved we are unable to return long distance telephone calls.

* *

TIME CONVERSION CHART

Below you will find a handy chart that allows you to convert local time to Coordinated Universal Time (U.T.C.). This used to be called Greenwich Mean Time or Zulu Time and is the international standard time usage based upon the Greenwhich meridian or 0° longitude line. The National Bureau of Standards maintains radio stations WWV in Fort Collins, Colorado and WWVH in Hawaii. On the frequencies of 2.5, 5.0, 10.0, 15.0, and 20.0 megahertz, the National Bureau of Standards broadcasts standard time signals that have an accuracy far greater than ever required in amateur radio.

WWV and WWVH broadcast signals continuosuly during each day. Each second is marked by a signal or tick. The 59th second signal is omitted intentionally. A voice announcement of the time is given each minute at the 55 second point and is followed by the tick on the minute. The announcement sounds like this:

"At the tone, sixteen hours fifty-nine minutes Coordinated Universal Time"

A lot of information is broadcast over WWV and you can get the details on what they do by writing them at:

Radio Station WWV
Fort Collins, Colorado 80524

TIME CONVERSION CHART

P.D.S.T.	M.D.S.T.	C.D.S.T	E.D.S.T.	U.T.C.	P.S.T.	M.S.T.	C.S.T.	E.S.T.
5 P.M.	6 P.M.	7 P.M.	8 P.M.	00:00	4 P.M.	5 P.M.	6 P.M.	7 P.M.
6 P.M.	7 P.M.	8 P.M.	9 P.M.	01:00	5 P.M.	6 P.M.	7 P.M.	8 P.M.
7 P.M.	8 P.M.	9 P.M.	10 P.M.	02:00	6 P.M.	7 P.M.	8 P.M.	9 P.M.
8 P.M.	9 P.M.	10 P.M.	11 P.M.	03:00	7 P.M.	8 P.M.	9 P.M.	10 P.M.
9 P.M.	10 P.M.	11 P.M.	Midnight	04:00	8 P.M.	9 P.M.	10 P.M.	11 P.M.
10 P.M.	11 P.M.	Midnight	1 A.M.	05:00	9 P.M.	10 P.M.	11 P.M.	Midnight
11 P.M.	Midnight	1 A.M.	2 A.M.	06:00	10 P.M.	11 P.M.	Midnight	1 A.M.
Midnight	1 A.M.	2 A.M.	3 A.M.	07:00	11 P.M.	Midnight	1 A.M.	2 A.M.
1 A.M.	2 A.M.	3 A.M.	4 A.M.	08:00	Midnight	1 A.M.	2 A.M.	3 A.M.
2 A.M.	3 A.M.	4 A.M.	5 A.M.	09:00	1 A.M.	2 A.M.	3 A.M.	4 A.M.
3 A.M.	4 A.M.	5 A.M.	6 A.M.	10:00	2 A.M.	3 A.M.	4 A.M.	5 A.M.
4 A.M.	5 A.M.	6 A.M.	7 A.M.	11:00	3 A.M.	4 A.M.	5 A.M.	6 A.M.
5 A.M.	6 A.M.	7 A.M.	8 A.M.	12:00	4 A.M.	5 A.M.	6 A.M.	7 A.M.
6 A.M.	7 A.M.	8 A.M.	9 A.M.	13:00	5 A.M.	6 A.M.	7 A.M.	8 A.M.
7 A.M.	8 A.M.	9 A.M.	10 A.M.	14:00	6 A.M.	7 A.M.	8 A.M.	9 A.M.
8 A.M.	9 A.M.	10 A.M.	11 A.M.	15:00	7 A.M.	8 A.M.	9 A.M.	10 A.M.
9 A.M.	10 A.M.	11 A.M.	Noon	16:00	8 A.M.	9 A.M.	10 A.M.	11 A.M.
10 A.M.	11 A.M.	Noon	1 P.M.	17:00	9 A.M.	10 A.M.	11 A.M.	Noon
11 A.M.	Noon	1 P.M.	2 P.M.	18:00	10 A.M.	11 A.M.	Noon	1 P.M.
Noon	1 P.M.	2 P.M.	3 P.M.	19:00	11 A.M.	Noon	1 P.M.	2 P.M.
1 P.M.	2 P.M.	3 P.M.	4 P.M.	20:00	Noon	1 P.M.	2 P.M.	3 P.M.
2 P.M.	3 P.M.	4 P.M.	5 P.M.	21:00	1 P.M.	2 P.M.	3 P.M.	4 P.M.
3 P.M.	4 P.M.	5 P.M.	6 P.M.	22:00	2 P.M.	3 P.M.	4 P.M.	5 P.M.
4 P.M.	5 P.M.	6 P.M.	7 P.M.	23:00	3 P.M.	4 P.M.	5 P.M.	6 P.M.

— NOTES —

— NOTES —

A NOTE TO CLASSROOM INSTRUCTORS

The Final Exam can be an asset to you for teaching theory. As you cover the syllabus you are using, please mention during the classroom instruction questions from this manual and then go on to explain the theory behind the question and answer. This way you are certain that you are covering the material that is being asked by the FCC.

What many instructors have done is to go through the manual and make up a reading list for their students. They tell the students to purchase The Final Exam along with their other study materials. You may say that this makes for a larger expenditure by the student but there is nothing cheap about ham radio, is there? No, of course not! Anyway, other instructors have typed up a reading list that goes along with their lectures.

For example, their list may say to review Questions 3, 14, 28, and 83 for Lesson #3. Again, you are covering the theory along with the practical aspects of passing the tests. I find far too many people who attended ham classes and spend their *time* and money (the time is usually more important) on the course and then failed the exam because the instructor didn't cover the material the FCC was asking about. It's great to have a background in theory but that doesn't count for much if you fail the FCC test. So, please help your students and help yourself by being certain that your lectures not only cover the theory you want your people to know but also cover the material the FCC is asking. That'll make your classes so successful you'll have a hard time refusing to do another class immediately!

As a note of interest, as an instructor you *should* have a copy of *Electronic Communication* by Robert L. Shrader. He presents radio theory in clear and easily readable words and also get as complex as you'd care to go. I recommend that students *and* instructors buy the manual. The only drawback is the cost: $19.50. But there's another case of the fact that ham radio is *not* inexpensive! The ARRL manuals are o.k. but, with a few noteworthy exceptions, they do not cover the theory so that the *average* ham can understand what they're trying to say. This isn't meant to be a criticism of the ARRL. They do some things *very* well: QSL bureaus, Field Day, awards, and other contests. But their licensing manuals are not the best. They could be a whole lot better. I have people call me all the time complaining about this. How the devil can the average housewife or other non-technical person be expected to make any sense of that? They can't and it shows up when they take the FCC exams. So, help your people by recommending that they buy Shrader's book. It is available through bookstores, from Ham Radio Bookstore (they're the folks who publish HR Reports and Ham Radio Horizons), or from us.

Together you and I can help the hams in their quest to upgrade. We *both* have an obligation to them because without them, where the hell would we be? For your additional info, I am working on a Novice theory book as well. Give me a call after October 1st to see what the status is. I promise you that it'll be a book a housewife can read and enjoy (no, I'm not a chauvinist pig; I *love* women and think we're not doing very much to help them get on the air and intend to change that). Good luck and call me if I can help you in any way.

— MORE PROPAGANDA & NEAT INFO —

Your support of our dealers is appreciated. Should your favorite dealer not be listed here (this list is current as of September 11, 1981), please have him contact us.

Most of these dealers began stocking our test guides because hams went to them and suggested that they carry the books. So you **do** have an effect upon the dealer. We can offer your dealer an attractive program and at the same time make our manuals available to you locally. **PLEASE** (would you believe "pretty please"?) tell your dealer about our test guides and other books and urge him to contact us at this address:

> Bash Educational services, Inc.
> P.O. Box 2115
> San Leandro, California 94577
> Telephone: 415-352-5420
> Attn: Dick Bash - KL7IHP

Thanks for all of **your** help and I wish you the very best when taking the FCC exam!

Reliable Electronics Anchorage, AK	Radio Place Sacramento, CA	Delaware Amateur Supply New Castle, DE	HI, Inc. Council Bluffs, IA
Long's Electronics Birmingham, AL	Selectronics Sacramento, CA	Amateur & Adv. Comm. Wilmington, DE	G & K Amateur Supply Des Moines, IA
Amatronics Millbrook, AL	Ham Radio Outlet San Diego, CA	Amateur Electronic Supply Clearwater, FL	Pebble Ranch Radio Post Falls, ID
Cobras Two-Way Supply Hope, AR	Pacific Marine Supply San Diego, CA	Ray's Amateur Radio Clearwater, FL	Ross Distributing Preston, ID
Pankey's TV Sales & Service Trumann, AR	Zack Electronics San Francisco, CA	Crane Electronics Fort Lauderdale, FL	Rick's Radio Repair Chicago, IL
Unger Television Apache Junction AZ	Hobbi-Tronics San Jose, CA	Mike's Electronics Fort Lauderdale, FL	Floyd Electronics Collinsville, IL
Masters Communications Glendale, AZ	Quement Electronics San Jose, CA 95150	Heathkit Electronic Center Hialeah, FL	Tri-State Electronic Corp. Mount Prospect, IL
Power Communications Phoenix AZ	Westcom San Marcos, CA	HeLP Radio Jacksonville, FL	Aureus Electronics Naperville, IL
Ham Radio Outlet Anaheim, CA	Hemec Communications Santa Barbara, CA	Amateur Radio Center Miami, FL	Spectronics Inc. Oak Park, IL
Ham Radio Outlet Burlingame, CA	Zac Kit/Vallejo Vallejo, CA	Bob's Amateur Radio Center Miami, FL	Johnson's Amateur Radio Supply Clarksville, IN
Base Station Concord, CA	Ham Radio Outlet Van Nuys, CA	N & G Distributing Miami, FL	The Ham Shack Evansville, IN
Jun Electronics Culver City, CA	Assoc. Electronic Serv. Colorado Springs, CO	Amateur Electronic Supply Inc. Orlando, FL	Kryder Electronics Fort Wayne, IN
Fontana Electronics Fontana, CA	CW Electronic Sales Co. Denver, CO	Quad Electronics Pensacola, FL	Graham Electronics Indianapolis, IN
Webster Radio Inc. Fresno, CA	Radio Service Center Denver, CO	CB Sales & Serv. Columbus, GA	Heathkit Electronic Center Indianapolis, IN
Dragnet Communications Glendora, CA	Hatry Electronics Hartford, CT	Radio Wholesale Columbus, GA	Hoosier Electronics Inc. Terre Haute, IN
Ham Radio Outlet Oakland, CA	Damon Electronics, Inc. Milford, CT	Britt's Two Way Radio Smyrna, GA	Quality TV/Radio Serv. Coffeyville, KS
Desert Haven Radio Ridgecrest, CA	Infocenter West Haven, CT	Honolulu Electronics Honolulu, HI	Amateur Radio Equipment Co. Wichita, KS

111

Cohoon Amateur Supply Inc.
Hopkinsville, KY

Heathkit Electronic Center
Louisville, KY

Heathkit Electronic Center
Kenner, LA

Tel-Com
Littleton, MA

Heathkit Electronic Center
Peabody, MA

Norbills Electronics Inc.
West Springfield, MA

Comm Center
Laurel, MD

Down-East Ham Shack
Auburn, ME

Sword Enterprises
Adrian, MI

DJ's Appliances
Allen Park, MI

RSE Ham Shack
Clawson, MI

Omar Electronics
Durand, MI

Midway Electronic Supply
990 West Eight Mile Road
Ferndale, MI

Radio Parts, Inc.
Grand Rapids, MI

Ferris Radio
Hazel Park, MI

HR Electronics
Muskegon, MI

Midwest Amateur Radio Supply
Minneapolis, MN

Heathkit Electronic Center
St. Paul, MN

Missouri Radio Center
Kansas City, MO

Mid-Com Electronics Inc.
St. Louis, MO

Conley Radio Supply
Billings, MT

Home - Tronics
Charlotte, NC

Brantley Electronic Supply, Inc.
Fayetteville, NC

Bino Communications Inc.
Greensboro, NC

F & M Electronics
Greensboro, NC

Joe's Communication
Rockingham, NC

Piedmont Amateur Radio Inc.
Rockwell, NC

Electronic Accessories Co.
Winston - Salem, NC

Don's Radio Communication
Wimbledon, ND

Comm Center Inc.
Lincoln, NE

Tufts Radio & Electronics
Hudson, NH

Hackensack, NJ

Wittie Electronics
Clifton, NJ

Broadcast Systems Company
Albuquerque, NM

Electronic Module
Hobbs, NM

Amateur Electronic Supply Inc.
Las Vegas, NV

Nevada CB & Stereo
Reno, NV

Ham Radio World
Oriskany, NY

Softron Systems
Rensselaer, NY

Heathkit Electronic Center
Rochester, NY

Ham - Bone Radio
Syracuse, NY

Brown Communications Co.
Akron, OH

Electronix Mart Inc.
Akron, OH

Northwest Electronics
Bellevue, OH

J.A.L. Amateur Radio
Canton, OH

Pioneer-Standard Electronics
Dayton, OH

Little Professor Book Center
New Philadelphia, OH

Universal Amateur Radio Inc.
Reynoldsburg, OH

Amateur Electronic Supply Inc.
Wickliffe, OH

Derrick Electronics Inc.
Broken Arrow, OK

Kryder Electronics
Oklahoma City, OK

Radio Inc.
Tulsa, OK

Oregon Ham Sales
Albany, OR

Eugene Radio Supply Inc.
Eugene, OR

Antronics of Oregon
Hillsboro, OR

Coleman Electronics
Medford, OR

Watt Shop
Oregon City, OR

Portland Radio Supply
Portland, OR

Donle Communications Inc.
Salem, OR

Amateur & C.B. Radio Supply
New Brighton, PA

Carr Electronics
Telford, PA

Hamtronics
Trevose, PA

JRS Distributors Inc.
York, PA

Centro Electronico
Aguadilla, PR

Radio Communications Systems
Caguas, PR

Abbe's Books & Hobbies
Ramey, PR

Heathkit Electronic Center
Warwick, RI

Sawyer Electronics, Inc.
Greenville, SC

Gismo Communications, Inc.
Rock Hill, SC

Burghardt Amateur Center
Watertown, SD

Rush Electronics Inc.
Bristol, TN

Doc's Communications
Lookout Mountain, TN

A.R.S.O.N.
Madison, TN

Germantown Amateur Supply Inc.
Memphis, TN

Sere-Rose Electronics Inc.
Memphis, TN

J-Tron Electronics
Springfield, TN

Douglas Electronics
Corpus Christi, TX

AGL Electronics
Dallas, TX

Hardin Electronics
Fort Worth, TX

Madison Electronics Supply
Houston, TX

Appliance & Eqpt. Co.
San Antonio, TX

R. L. Cole Electronics
San Antonio, TX

Dolphin Electronics
Seabrook, TX

Heathkit Electronic Center
Midvale, UT

Mack Communications
Roosevelt, UT

Distributors Inc.
Portsmouth, VA

Electronic Eqpt. Bank
Vienna, VA

Electronics Unlimited Inc.
St. Thomas, VI

A.B.C. Communications
Seattle, WA

Amateur Radio Supply
Seattle, WA

C-Comm
Seattle, WA

Mercer & Son
Shelton, WA

Radio Shop
Spokane, WA

Mount Tahoma Enterprizes
Tacoma, WA

Northwest Radio Supply
Tacoma, WA

Anderson Electronics
Eau Claire, WI

Amateur Electronic Supply Inc
Milwaukee, WI

CLS Communications
Ravenswood, WV

ALL ABOUT YOUR CALL SIGN

If you want to apply for a call sign change (and I suggest you do), you must do so at the time of application for upgrading. Check box 2F on your FCC Form 610. The FCC will then issue you a new call sign in the appropriate format.

Eligibility and application procedures for call sign changes are explained in the FCC news release dated March 30, 1978, which is available at FCC field offices. The call sign groups are listed below, followed by a summary of licensee eligibility. If you hold no license at the time of application, you will automatically be issued a license call sign in the appropriate format. For example, if you have no license and go pass the combined 70 question FCC exam plus their 5 w.p.m. code test, you will be issued a Technician Class license and the call sign will be in the 1 x 3 format (Group C). Applicants for a Novice Class license will automatically be issued a call sign in the 2 x 3 format (Group D). If you would like to know what call signs are currently being issued, please give us a telephone call.

CALL SIGN FORMATS NOW BEING ISSUED

Group A   2 x 1 call signs (for Extra Class *only*), such as NR6X
Group B   2 x 2 call signs (for Advanced and Extra *only*), such as KB6VD
Group C   1 x 3 call signs (for General/Technician, Advanced, or Extra), such as N6QRT
Group D   2 x 3 call signs (for all licensees), such as KA6LRP

ELIGIBILITY

Licensees upgrading to:	May change:
Novice Class	Group D only
Technician Class	from Group D to Group C call sign
General Class	from Group D to Group C call sign

Advanced Class	from Group D to Groups C **or** B
Advanced Class	from Group C to Group B call sign
Extra Class	from Group D to Groups C, B, **or** A
Extra Class	from Group C to Groups B **or** A
Extra Class	from Group B to Group A call sign

Changes to any of the above procedures will be announced by the FCC.

REVISION POLICY

Occasionally we have a sufficient number of changes and/or new questions to warrant the issuance of a revision for the manual. This material is available to you by sending us a self addressed stamped envelope (SASE) with 35¢ in stamps on it plus $2.00 to cover costs of duplication, etc. In the lower left hand corner of the SASE please write the name of the revision (General, Advanced, or Extra).

However, how do you know if there is a revision available before you go trotting off to the FCC exam room? You simply telephone us and ask whoever answers the phone if there is a revision for your manual. We'll need to know which manual you have and how long ago you got it (that'll tell us how many revisions apply to your specific case). If there is a revision, we'll tell you to shoot us the two bucks, SASE, etc. Please be sure to call *not less than 2 weeks before you take the exam!* This is to allow time for the mail system. Please don't call the girls the day before the test and ask if there's anything new. So, that's all there is to it! Nothing difficult about that, was there?

Order Form

(Don't copy this book, darn it! We need the $$$)

Name _____

Call Sign _____

Address _____

City _____ State _____ Zip _____

☐ **Novice Class** (4.95 each) $ _____

☐ **General Class** (9.95 each) $ _____

☐ **Advanced Class** (9.95 each) $ _____

☐ **Extra Class** (9.95 each) $ _____

☐ **Band-Aids** (9.95 each) $ _____

☐ **The Complete Idiot's Guide to DX** (9.95 each) $ _____

☐ **The DX-Pediter** (29.95 each) $ _____

Sales tax of 6 1/2 % if in California $ _____

Postage and handling (see below) $ _____

Total amount enclosed $ _____

Send your order to:

Bash Educational Services, Inc.
P.O. Box 2115
San Leandro, CA 94577
415-352-5420

How to figure shipping:

Please add $2.25 per book for 1st Class mailing of *The Final Exam's* and *Band-Aids* and $2.50 per copy of *The Complete Idiot's Guide to DX*. Add only $2.00 for 1st Class mailing of *The Dx-Pediter. The Dx-Pediter* is a disk based program for the Apple II (or II+) that serves to log DX contacts for the ARRL's DXCC award. Pretty neat program!

If ordering C.O.D., please note that we'll ship C.O.D.'s only within the 48 States and only via UPS Brown Label, which normally takes 5-7 working days to reach you. All orders are shipped within 48 hours of receipt.

WRITE & ASK FOR OUR CATALOG OF FINE BOOKS!

Order Form

(Don't copy this book, darn it! We need the $$$)

Name _____

Call Sign _____

Address _____

City _____ State _____ Zip _____

☐ **Novice Class** (4.95 each) $ _____

☐ **General Class** (9.95 each) $ _____

☐ **Advanced Class** (9.95 each) $ _____

☐ **Extra Class** (9.95 each) $ _____

☐ **Band-Aids** (9.95 each) $ _____

☐ **The Complete Idiot's Guide to DX** (9.95 each) $ _____

☐ **The DX-Pediter** (29.95 each) $ _____

Sales tax of 6 1/2 % if in California $ _____

Postage and handling (see below) $ _____

Total amount enclosed $ _____

Send your order to:

> **Bash Educational Services, Inc.**
> **P.O. Box 2115**
> **San Leandro, CA 94577**
> **415-352-5420**

How to figure shipping:

Please add $2.25 per book for 1st Class mailing of *The Final Exam's* and *Band-Aids* and *$2.50 per copy of The Complete Idiot's Guide to DX.* Add only $2.00 for 1st Class mailing of *The Dx-Pediter. The Dx-Pediter* is a disk based program for the Apple II (or II +) that serves to log DX contacts for the ARRL's DXCC award. Pretty neat program!

If ordering C.O.D., please note that we'll ship C.O.D.'s only within the 48 States and only via UPS Brown Label, which normally takes 5-7 working days to reach you. All orders are shipped within 48 hours of receipt.

WRITE & ASK FOR OUR CATALOG OF FINE BOOKS!

BASH EDUCATIONAL SERVICES, INC.

GENERAL CLASS EDITION
ERRATA SHEET

"To err is human.." Well, in keeping with the practice of being human, we also err once in awhile! Below you will find those errors that we've caught. Should you find others, please write and tell us about them.

Page 17 Question 13   You *will* see the FCC use "peak reverse voltage," so be ready for it.

Page 24 Question 26   We *didn't* goof here! Just want to let you know that if the FCC tells you that it's an **A.M.** transmitter, then you would hear a **clear and normal voice signal**.

Page 40 Question 57   In item J, change the 48 mA to 224 mA. In item K right below that, change 66 volts to 6 volts.

Page 59 Question 100   Don't know what I could have been thinking of here. In the question, please change the word "reactance" to **inductance.**

Page 62 Question 112   Eliminate this question and answer altogether because it is no longer on the test and we have it shown incorrectly also. One less to worry about, right?

Page 62 Question 114   In the middle of the answer, I have a typographical error. Please change 486 ÷ 145 to 468 ÷ 145.

Page 64 Question 115   In the last sentence of the answer, I made a dumb typing error. Change "2 dB" to **3** dB.

Page 65 Question 120   I must have dozed off at this point! Those frequencies should all be megahertz instead of kilohertz. Change all the K's to M's.

Page 72 Question 142   In item e, please change the 0.80 to 0.66.

That covers all of the booboos I made! Next we have some modified questions and some new items. Please be sure to go over these ten (10) times as well!

NEW QUESTIONS
(as of July 1, 1982)

1. During daylight hours, 80 meter radio waves are affected how?

   They are almost completely absorbed by the D layer of the ionosphere.

2. Which of the following statements best describes a characteristic of a radio frequency signal produced by *amplitude modulation*? (This replaces Questions 91 and 94).

   The instantaneous amplitude (envelope) of the radio frequency signal varies in accordance with the modulating audio frequency signal.

3. What happens to radio wave propagation when a *sudden ionospheric disturbance* (SID) occurs?

   All daylight ionospheric propagation of high frequency radio waves stops abruptly and then gradually returns to normal within about *40 minutes*.

4. Two meter radio waves (144 - 148 MHz) often may be propagated beyond the line-of-sight distance because of what phenomena?

   Scatter.

5. What can you expect to occur if an amplitude modulated emission is being *overmodulated*?

   There will be periods of time when the transmitter radio frequency (RF) energy output is zero, causing distortion and splatter.

6. Which of the following definitions are associated with the word *impedance*?

   It is the opposition to the flow of an alternating current in an electrical circuit containing both resistance and reactance.

7.	A transmitter with a solid state, transistorized final amplifier is found to draw a current of 15 amperes from a 12 volt regulated power supply when the key is held closed. Based upon these given values, what is the *input power to the final amplifier* of this particular transmitter?

The formula to use here is $P = I \times E$. In this case, you would substitute the values that were given and get $P = 15 \times 12$. That works out to 180 watts!

8.	*Audio rectification interference* occurs when an audio frequency amplifier (such as an electric organ, public address system, etc.) responds to radio frequency signals. What best describes what would probably be heard from an electric organ responding to the signal from an amateur radio station that was transmitting **single sideband** voice emissions? (Note: this replaces Question 26; Question 27 is still valid and *always* follows this one!).

It would be distorted/garbled and practically unintelligible.

9.	*Audio rectification interference* occurs when an audio frequency amplifier (such as an electric organ, public address system, etc.) responds to radio frequency signals. What best describes what would probably be heard from an electric organ responding to the signal from an amateur radio station that was transmitting **amplitude modulated** voice emissions?

It would be a clear and normal voice signal. *Note that you may get* **either** *this one or the previous one. Question 27 is usually found to follow this one on the exam also. Make sure you have the clear distinction between these two similar questions: this one is talking about AM and the other is about SSB.*

10.	Please make certain you know the definitions of A3 and F3 emissions. A3 is amplitude modulated radiotelephony (AM voice) and F3 is frequency modulated radiotelephony (FM voice).

11.	Delete the answer to Question 63 and replace it with the single word **SCATTER.** This refers to "troposcatter" and to "backscatter."

★★

This completes our update. Please note that if you intend to take the combined Novice-General written exam at the FCC office (the 70 question exam) that 20 of the 70 questions will be Novice type questions and can be found in the latest copy of the Novice Class edition of *The*

Final Exam. Also please be very careful when taking the FCC's 13 w.p.m. code test. There is a persistent rumor that there are *deliberate* misspellings on some of the code tests. **It would benefit everyone if you would please send the contents of your code exams in to us.** Knowing the code is no guarantee you'll pass the FCC's code test. It is a 10 question, fill-in-the-blank type of exam (as of July, 1982) and is in a QSO format. We have put all the feedback on the code tests we've received onto a cassette tape and called it *The Final Exam's Final Code Course.* Order a copy of our 13 w.p.m. QSO code tape ($9.95 plus $2.00 for 1st class mailing) and you'll be ok. It's very, very accurate! Tell your friends that we also have a 5 w.p.m. and 20 w.p.m. tape available.

Don't forget to telephone our offices not less than **2 weeks** before you take the exam to find out if there is anything new. That 2 weeks gives us time to get any new material to you! If we have a revision, the way to get it is to send us a self addressed stamped envelope (SASE) with 37¢ in postage on it plus $2.00. Use a business size envelope for your SASE and put the words GENERAL CLASS REVISION in the lower left hand corner of it.

Be sure to use the latest copy of the FCC 610 Form when you apply for your license. If you don't have a copy of it, send us an SASE (with a 20¢ stamp on it) and we'll send you one! The current form in use is dated August, 1980. If you wish to change your call sign and get one of the new ones (which I recommend), mark box 2F on the form along with completing the other information. Don't forget to take a photocopy of your license (if you have been issued one) with you to the FCC office.

Once you pass your exam, if you previously held a Novice Class license, you will be issued an Interim Permit. Until you receive your permanent copy of the license from the FCC, you are required to identify your call sign along with the words "Interim XX" when operating voice and "/XX" (the stroke is DN in code) when operating CW on frequencies other than the Novice bands. The "XX" will be the two letter designator for the FCC Field Office that administered your test, such as AT for Atlanta, SF for San Francisco, BS for Boston, etc. So, if it was me, I'd say "this is KL7IHP interim SF" when using voice and "de KL7IHP/SF" when using CW.

Please help another person interested in ham radio get started. We have managed to get our manuals tape recorded for the blind. If a blind person needs our manuals, have him/her contact Mr. Vernon Henley, c/o Oklahoma Radio Reading Service, 1108 Northeast 36th Street, Oklahoma City, OK 73111. The tapes are at a special speed and won't work on a regular cassette recorder. The National Braille Association, 5300 Hamilton Avenue - Suite 1404, Cincinnati, OH 45224 (attention: Mrs. Lawrence M. Levine) has the Advanced and General manuals in Braille and will soon have the Novice in Braille as well.

Every once in awhile all of us here at Bash Educational Services go on a DXpedition (such as the one to Montserrat where I operated as VP2MMR in August, 1981 or to Kwajalein as KX6BU in April, 1980). If you hear of us going on one, give a shout! We'll be happy to confirm a DX contact for you. We should be going to somewhere in the Pacific about April, 1983. If you're having difficulty learning about DX, order a copy of *The Complete Idiot's Guide to DX.*" This was written by Stu Gregg - NF4Z and explains all the secrets and tricks to working DX. It'll be a valuable addition to your library and it tells you things even your friends won't tell you! It sells for $12.45 ($9.95 plus $2.50 for 1st Class mailing). Also for the DX'er we have a floppy disk based program for use with an Apple computer that logs DX contacts. It's called *The DX-PEDITER* and was written by Fred Pearlman - WD0DLM. It sells for $29.95 plus $2.00 for 1st Call mailing.

We recently published a book called *Band-Aids* by James E. Dersch - KB7FT. In many ways this is a whole ham library in one volume. It is filled with lots of maps, charts, tables, addresses, operator tips, etc. It's sort of an encyclopedia of miscellaneous information for hams. You won't want to be without one of these! It sells for $12.20 ($9.95 plus $2.25 for 1st Class mailing).

I go to about 2 hamfests a month around the country, so if I'm going to be at one near you, stop by the booth and say hi! It's fun to meet the people we correspond with throughout the year. If you've never been to a hamfest before, try it. The granddaddy of them all is the Dayton Hamvention in Dayton, Ohio. It's held the last weekend of April at Dayton's Hara Arena. There are always about 25,000 wild and crazy hams there talking about ham radio 29 hours a day! The exhibits are great and the fleamarket is unlike anything you can imagine.

Lastly, I want to say thank you for purchasing my manual and I wish you every success in passing the exam. We are experiencing about an 85% - 90% passing rate at this time (10% - 15% of the population doesn't seem to be able to pass *anything*, but that's something for our school systems to deal with). Our manuals are accurate because people like yourself sent us their feedback cards. Please be sure to send yours in so we can stay on top of things.

Scratch Paper

Scratch Paper

Scratch Paper

And God said...

$$\frac{mv^2}{r} = \frac{Z\,e^2}{r^2}$$

$$mvr = \frac{nh}{2\pi}$$

$$r = \frac{r^2\,h^2}{(2\pi)^2\,m\,Z\,e^2}$$

$$E = \frac{1}{2}\,mv^2 - Z\,\frac{e^2}{r}$$

$$E = \frac{2\pi\,m\,Z^2\,e^4}{n^2\,h^2} = Ry$$

...and there was Light.

Tomorrow is brought to you by Bash Educational Services—today!

P.O. Box 2115 • San Leandro, California 94577 • 415/352-5420

FEEDBACK

Name_____ Callsign_____

Address _____

City_____ State_____ Zip_____

I took my General/Advanced/Extra Class exam (circle where applicable) at the F.C.C.

office in _____ on _____. My examination number

(shown somewhere on the cover page of the test) was _____. Each
question had a choice of four/five (cross out where applicable) answers.
I ☐ Passed   ☐ Failed

I recall the following question(s) were on my test:

1. _____

_____

_____

2. _____

_____

_____

3. _____

_____

FEEDBACK

1801**G**

Name_____ Callsign_____

Address _____

City_____ State_____ Zip_____

I took my General/Advanced/Extra Class exam (circle where applicable) at the F.C.C.

office in _____ on _____. My examination number

(shown somewhere on the cover page of the test) was _____. Each
question had a choice of four/five (cross out where applicable) answers.
I ☐ Passed   ☐ Failed

I recall the following question(s) were on my test:

1. _____

_____

_____

2. _____

_____

_____

3. _____

_____

BASH EDUCATIONAL SERVICES
P.O. BOX 2115
SAN LEANDRO, CALIFORNIA 94577

Place stamp here.
The Post Office
will not deliver
mail without
postage.

BASH EDUCATIONAL SERVICES
P.O. BOX 2115
SAN LEANDRO, CALIFORNIA 94577